The Daily Telegraph
Chess Puzzles

International Grandmaster
David Norwood

B. T. Batsford Ltd, London

First published 1995
© David Norwood 1995

ISBN 0 7134 7815 2

British Library Cataloguing-in-Publication Data.
A catalogue record for this book is
available from the British Library.

Typeset by John Nunn
and printed in Great Britain by
Redwood Books, Trowbridge, Wilts
for the publishers,
B. T. Batsford Ltd,
4 Fitzhardinge Street,
London W1H 0AH

Contents

Foreword

'It was a book to kill time, for those who like it better dead.'
Rose Macaulay 1889-1918

'A beginning, a muddle and an end.'
Philip Larkin 1922-85 – a 'classic formula' for a book.

I have never found writing a book an easy task. I have particular problems with beginnings. Signing the contract is easy; spending the advance even easier. But putting finger to keyboard for that first chapter is nearly impossible. Confucius wrote that a journey of a thousand miles begins with the first step. He might have added that the first step is the one most likely to set you off in the wrong direction. What's more, in making that first step you commit yourself to a journey of hard work and more hard work.

If you don't believe me, we can consider the problem in terms of a chess game. The master turns up to the board, his clock is ticking and he must make the first move. He has known the name of his opponent from the day before, leaving hours to dwell on his strategy. His first move he has played hundreds of times for a decade. Yet still there is hesitation. I once saw a Polish master ponder for 67 minutes on move 1!

Even when we know the beginning, making a start can still prove tough.

Telling publishers how well the start is going is very easy, but ultimately there has to be a day of reckoning. I once delayed a book for six years but they won in the end. This book only got started because of a sudden inspiration. The book would be divided in two. The first half would be reality: real puzzles that had occurred in the course of real games. The other would be fantasy: puzzles which had been dreamt up by weird and wonderful minds. I was so pleased with this solution that I awarded myself a further fortnight's rest.

Not only is writing two smaller books easier than one big one, but there are other attractions. The theme of duality is mirrored in everyday life. Things happen, and then there are things that might have happened, or which we wanted to happen, or which happened in dreams. All very philosophical for a chess player, but I like the idea anyway.

David Norwood
International Grandmaster
St Martin (Caribbean), April 1995,
with Cathy Bushell
(Miss Australia 1988)

Symbols and Notation

In this book I have adopted a system of notation that will be familiar to readers of my weekly column in *The Daily Telegraph*. The system is so simple that even those few people who have never read my column will be able to pick it up in minutes.

Consider the following diagram:

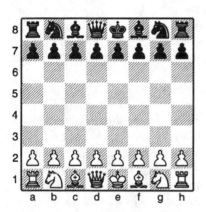

A move is indicated by the square where the piece starts, followed by the one where it lands. This is preceded, for all except pawn moves, by a figurine for the piece moving:

♔ king
♕ queen
♖ rook
♗ bishop
♘ knight

I have used few other symbols throughout this book. Some highly technical chess books are covered with hieroglyphics; this is not one of them. There is one symbol I have had to use a lot; it is very important:

\# checkmate

Please memorise this one. A few other symbols also crop up:

x   captures
+   check
++   double check
0-0   castles kingside
0-0-0 castles queenside
...   a move by Black
!!   brilliant move
!   good move
?   bad move
??   horrible blunder
1-0   Black resigns
½-½   Draw
0-1   White resigns

And a few more, to show the type of event where a game was played:

Ct   Candidates event
Ch   Championship
Z   Zonal
Cht   Team championship
corr Postal game

Introduction

The what's and why's of 'chess puzzles'

If everything ran smoothly, life would be boring. Probably the main reason the world is in such a mess is because we like problems. We relish the challenge, and the feeling of success when we overcome a challenge. The greater the challenge, the greater the thrill. In the world of professional chess there are certain top grandmasters who declare that winning is all-important. A point is a point on the tournament scoreboard.

But this is only partly true. There is little satisfaction in an effortless victory. Only epic struggles give real pleasure, where your wily opponent has thrown every possible problem at you. And you've solved them all, and won. A chess game is a myriad of problems. Entwining the grand strategic themes of the royal game are a great many little fiddly bits. Tricks and traps which can suddenly turn a game upside-down. Some group them under the heading 'tactics'.

When I was a young chess player, people referred to me as a 'tactician' – if they were being kind. Others dubbed me a 'swindler'. I overheard one player warning a prospective opponent about me: 'You will easily outplay him strategically, but beware of his tactics.' It was as if tactics were the antithesis to strategy, like chaos to order. Some years later, at the Soviet Chess School in Moscow, I was informed that perfect chess is a harmony between strategic play and tactical blows.

How do tricks and tactics relate to chess puzzles? Chess puzzles, almost by definition, have a tactical theme. The solution usually requires doing something slightly unusual. Something fiddly or tricky. If it didn't, then it wouldn't be much of a puzzle. But as we shall see later, defining what is 'usual' in chess is a problem in itself. A battle of semantics is something to be avoided. For our purposes, I want to define a chess puzzle as follows:

A specific problem on a chessboard (which need not have arisen from an actual game) requiring a specific solution.

I say 'specific problem', because there is usually a stipulation. It may just be White to play and win; it may be White to play and checkmate in five moves. Or it could be White to play and give checkmate in twenty moving his knight only.

I say 'specific solution' because there is usually, although not always, a set way of play. In a real game, White may be winning in general terms. A puzzle is more specific; the situation is critical and a particular set of moves is required.

'Puzzle' is the best general heading. It's certainly the safest because otherwise the whole thing can become rather too academic. While a 'problem' is a puzzle, the reverse is not necessarily the case. A problem is a composition (i.e. not from a real game) with a specific stipulation such as 'White to play and mate in three'. The good news is that you don't need to know all the jargon in order to enjoy them.

Enjoyment is certainly the main reason why people spend time over puzzles. However, puzzles can also benefit your over-the-board play. Even though the number of different types of positions that can arise in a chess game is astronomical, the number of tactical themes is quite limited: decoy, deflection, clearance, zwischenzug, and a handful of others. Again, you don't need to know the names but you will soon see their practical application in Part 1. You will probably find that the first half of this book, where puzzles are taken from real game situations, will be of more benefit in improving your play.

You must never think that solving a chess puzzle is the same as spotting a winning combination in a real game. The difference, and this is key, is that in a puzzle you are told specifically what to look for. There are many demon puzzle solvers who miss even the most elementary tactics when it comes to real chess. This is because in any given position they do not know whether there is a tactic or not. And they do not have time to conduct an in-depth search after every move.

This is the wrong approach. The trick is to learn to sense the kind of positions where there may be a tactic. This is the skill of the master tactician, and the amateur will admire this as an innate, almost supernatural talent. The truth is that this skill can be developed. When you try your hand at the puzzles in Part 1, look at the *type* of positions where the tactics occur. The same patterns occur time and time again, and the more you can commit to memory, the easier it will be to sense a similar prototype.

How to use this book

As I cheerfully boasted in the Foreword, this book is divided into two distinct parts. Part 1 consists of real game situations, where you take the place of some famous Champion or even just A.N. Other to spot a winning (or drawing) combination. We will start with simple mates-in-one.

Puzzles involving a clear goal (e.g. checkmate) remain the most popular and in many ways the most aesthetically pleasing. In Chapters 4 and 5 the puzzles are less rigid; the aim may be to win decisive material or to find a way to force a draw. Those wishing to improve their tactical ability should pay particular attention to these chapters.

Part 2 is quite different. All the positions are composed; they have been created by human ingenuity. Every piece has been placed on the board for some purpose, practical or aesthetic. This factor in itself can often provide a clue to the solution. If you can work out why one obscure piece is placed where it is, this could help you crack the problem. These puzzles are less likely to improve your over-the-board play but for many problem lovers they are an end in themselves.

The main aim of compositions is aesthetic, both for composer and solver. For many years I spurned problems. They were too difficult and had no practical purpose. As Professor George Steiner put it, 'Problems are like masturbation ... whereas playing chess is like making love.' No wonder the problemists tend to be an esoteric bunch. Yet whatever the auto-erotic implications, chess problems can be a lot of fun, and I've become a convert. It is high time that problems emerged from a world of inaccessible jargon to take their deserved place in the chess world.

Each problem will have a composer and date next to it. If this information is absent, it will mean that I don't know the origin. In the past I have been taken to task for not acknowledging a composer. Given the time and energy that has been devoted to the composition this seems only fair, and I would ask any reader wishing to reproduce them to bear it in mind.

On the more difficult puzzles I have tried to assist the reader with a *CLUE*. But it should be stressed that puzzles require time and concentration. I have spent hours and hours agonising over some of the puzzles in this book. I once received a letter from an exasperated *Daily Telegraph* reader: '... please tell me the solution, which has eluded myself, my wife and my computer for several months ...'. So if you find yourself stumped, don't immediately flick to the answers.

All that remains is to wish you GOOD LUCK!

1 Checkmate in One

'Chess is a testy, cholericke game, and very offensive to him that loseth the mate.'
Robert Burton 1577-1640

This chapter needs little introduction. You have a diagram position, you are told who is to move, and you have to find the immediate checkmate – it really couldn't be easier. But if you have never solved a chess puzzle before, there is certainly no better introduction. When I was six years old my bedtime reading consisted of solving a whole chapter of mates in one. When I had finally mastered all the mates in one in sight, I boldly moved on to the mates in two.

The chapter ends with three rather amusing positions; those who have become contemptuous of 'Mate in One' puzzles might do well to look at them. In fact, the final position occurred while I was writing this book. I wonder whether it was divine intervention to make this chapter less banal. Either way, my embarrassing moment happened in front of around fifty German spectators, all of whom were thinking the same thing: how could a grandmaster miss a mate in one?

1   **Bagirov-Csom**
     Palma 1989

White to play and mate in one.
The queen and knight often work
in harmony.

2   **Knaak-Vujosević**
     Budapest 1988

White to play and mate in one.

3   **Szalanczy-Leko**
     Budapest 1993

Black to play and mate in one.

4   **Wojtkiewicz-Ftačnik**
     Budapest Z 1993

Black to play and mate in one.

5   **Zapata-Vilela**
Capablanca mem 1993

White to play and mate in one. White could capture the rook but that would be boring.

6   **Grosar-Schroll**
Graz Z 1993

White to play and mate in one. It looks as if the white king is in trouble but it's all under control.

7   **Mok Tze Meng-Reilly**
Djakarta Z 1993

White to play and mate in one.

8   **Maksimenko-Savon**
Nikolaev Z 1993

Black to play and mate in one.

9 A.Ivanov-Yermolinsky
USA Ch 1993

White to play and mate in one, but White still lost the game.

10 Short-Beliavsky
Linares 1992

Nigel Short, World Championship candidate, could have played 1 ♔e5-d4 with an advantage thanks to his passed b-pawn. However, Short likes to advance, and played 1 ♔e5-e6. What had he missed?

11 Lputian-Norwood
Lvov 1986

I spent some fifteen minutes wondering whether to move my king to d7 or c7. Being unhappy with both moves, I decided to opt for a bold advance (1...♔d6-d5). Rather too bold, as it happens...

12 Piskov-Norwood
Bundesliga 1995

    1 ...   ♘d8-e6
After this I thought there were good chances for a draw. After all, 2 d4-d5 ♘e6-c5 is mate, and both the d- and h-pawns are attacked. Why was I so badly wrong?

Solutions

(1)
   1 ♕e3-h6#

(2)
   1 ♕h5-e5#

(3)
   1 ...   ♖f3-f4#

(4)
   1 ...   ♕f3-h1#
The queen cannot be taken because the knight is pinned.

(5)
   1 ♘d6-b7#
The alternative mate 1 ♘d6-c4# is equally good.

(6)
   1 ♘a6-b4#

(7)
   1 ♗f5-g4# (or 1 ♕f6-h6#)

(8)
   1 ...   ♖c8-c4#

(9)
   1 ♕h5-h8#
White's flag fell after making his previous move (his 37th) and the arbiter declared it a win for Black, even though White had mated Black.

(10)
   1 ♔e5-e6
This advance is natural enough, but for one fatal flaw. Retreating moves are the hardest to spot but here it was worth a second look.
   1 ...   ♗b7-c8#

(11)
   1 ...   ♔d6-d5
   2 ♖e1-e5#
When my opponent played this move, he muttered something. I assumed he'd offered a draw so I reached out to accept. Suddenly it dawned on me that I had just been mated.

(12)
   2 ♘b6-d5#

2 Checkmate in Two

'Chess is ruthless: you've got to be prepared to kill people.'
Nigel Short

Rather like the first chapter, the aim is easy to grasp: find a way to force checkmate in two moves. So you need to develop your skills at finding a quick one-two. The first move is usually the hard one to spot. It may be that you have lots of ways to check the king, but the solution demands a quiet, subtle move. Often it's good a idea to focus on the enemy king's flight squares, and to ensure that you cut them off. I tend to see this as 'closing the coffin lid' – rather macabre but not a bad analogy.

Most of the puzzles, though, require drama, particularly sacrifices. The queen sacrifice remains the most popular theme in mate in two puzzles. There is something so aesthetically pleasing about the sacrifice of one's most powerful piece that it is hard to buck this trend. Certain mad psychologists have argued that chess contains a sublimated Oedipal complex, where we indulge our latent passion for father murder. But chess players seem to be so obsessed with

sacrificing their lady that my hunch is that the psychologists have got it all mixed up.

The mate in two puzzle strikes a tragic chord in my own heart. The most beautiful game that I have ever played was against Russian Grandmaster Vadim Ruban in Calcutta 1990. After some dazzling sacrifices, we reached the following position.

Now I played 1 ♕f5-d3+ and after a string of blunders I managed to lose. After the game a little Indian boy pointed out a better continuation:

    1   ♕f5-f4+   ♔d6xc5
    2   ♕f4-d4#

That's why I'm not so keen on mates in two!

1 **Hebden-Pichon**
Cappelle la Grande 1990

White to play and mate in two. Here English grandmaster Mark Hebden played 1 ♕f7-g6 and gave mate next move on h7, but he could have pleased the crowd even more. How?

2 **Hall-King**
Norrköping 1988

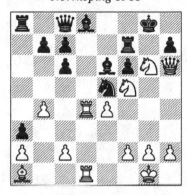

Here the British GM/TV Commentator found himself in a sticky patch. In fact, his opponent found a way to force mate in two. How?

3 **Bernstein-Kotov**
Groningen 1946

White to play and mate in two. It looks as if the white king is the one in trouble, but there is a 'visual' way to end the fight.

4 **Wells-Zso.Polgar**
Budapest 1993

White to play and mate in two. Every man's dream is to mate a Polgar and here Grandmaster Peter Wells seizes his chance. How does he make use of the extra queen?

5   **Seret-Löffler**
         Cannes 1993

White to play and mate in two. Rook, knight and bishop combine to form an efficient mating net.

6   **Nimzowitsch-Alapin**
         Karlsbad 1911

White to play and mate in two. Nimzowitsch has invested a piece; how does he demand pay-back?

7   **Viakhirev-Alekhine**
         corr 1907

Black to play and mate in two. It looks as if White has withstood the assault and the black queen is trapped in the corner. However, the great master of attack is not so easily outwitted.

8   **Nimzowitsch-Tarrasch**
       St. Petersburg 1914

Black to play and mate in two. This time it's Nimzo's turn to suffer. What is the most efficient method to trap the white king?

9   Dubinin-Botvinnik
USSR Ch (Leningrad) 1939

Black to play and mate in two. It was a rare sight to see Botvinnik a full queen down but here he has good reason. This position must have been a knightmare for White.

10   Timman-Short
Tilburg 1990

White to play and mate in two. This is the oldest mate in the book, but it still sufficed to defeat England's former number one, Nigel Short.

11   Savon-Polugaevsky
USSR Ch (Leningrad) 1971

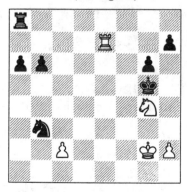

White to play. It is hard to imagine that mate is in the air but a quiet move is all that is needed to force either mate or a decisive material gain.

12   Capablanca-Steiner
Los Angeles 1933

White to play and win. The great genius Capablanca has sacrificed a rook for a raging attack. How to you force either mate in two or the win of Black's queen?

Solutions

(1)

  1 ♕f7-g8+   ♖f8xg8
  2 ♘g5-f7#

(2)

  1 ♕h6-g7+   ♖f7xg7
  2 ♘f5-h6#

(3)

  1 ♕d2xh6+   g7xh6
  2 ♖a8-g8#

(4)

  1 ♕e6xf7+   ♔g6-f5
  2 ♕d8-d7 (or c8)#

(5)

  1 ♘g5-f7+   ♔h8-h7
  2 ♖g6-g7#

(6)

  1 ♕d2-d8+!!   ♗e7xd8
  2 ♖e1-e8#

(7)

  1 ...   ♕h1-g2+
  2 ♖h2xg2   f3xg2#

(8)

  1 ...   ♖f8-e8+
  2 ♔e6-d7   ♗f1-b5#

(9)

  1 ...   ♘d4-f3+
  2 ♔g1-f1   ♘e4-d2#

(10)

  1 ♕c4-g8+   ♖e8xg8
  2 ♘h6-f7#

(11)

  1 ♔g2-g3

Black can only prevent mate next move at the cost of a great deal of material. His king cannot run:

  1 ...   ♔g5-f5
  2 ♖e7-e5#

(12)

  1 ♖f6xc6+!

White now mops up, since Black cannot take the rook:

  1 ...   ♕b6xc6
  2 ♕b7-b4#

3 Checkmate in Three or More

'Sure, winning isn't everything. It's
the only thing.'
Henry 'Red' Sanders 1958

The king-hunt is probably the most
thrilling part of a chess game. The
desire to hunt is one of the most
primeval instincts in man. However,
a chess master must exercise re-
straint in most stages of the game;
subtle manoeuvring, rather than the
direct charge, is usually the way to
victory. Our abstinence, though, is
disingenuous, merely an opportun-
istic measure to notch up more
points. On the chess board the desire
to be the hunter is sublimated, but
never eradicated. This is precisely
why it is all that more ecstatic when
we do get a chance to go in for the
kill.

The cleanest, and sweetest, kill
is checkmate. A resignation before
one delivers the *coup de grâce* can
be irksome. A violent fight once
broke out between two top French
international masters after one had
been checkmated. The reason? The
winner alleged that the vanquished
had entered in his game score that he
had resigned *before* the mate had
been delivered.

Hopefully, this chapter will not
provoke any violent outbursts. The
aim of the puzzles is to find a continuation that leads, by force, to
checkmate. Good luck, but keep
your fists to yourself.

1 Osborne-Contin
Bern 1992

Black to play and mate in three. White has nearly co-ordinated his material advantage; nearly, but not quite. How did Black ensure that any relief was short-lived?

2 Varavin-Zavarnitsin
USSR 1991

White to play and force mate. This is quite a tough puzzle, but I will give you the hint that the main line is seven moves long and the fourth move is the trickiest.

3 Kamsky-Yusupov
Tilburg 1993

Black to play and mate in three. This isn't such a tricky one but it's not every day that we get to see Gata Kamsky checkmated!

4 Magem Badals-Karpov
Madrid 1992

White played 1 ♕b2-b7, leaving Black with mate in three. How did Anatoly Karpov use a well-known theme to set up a mating net?

5   Jansson-Ivarsson
1973

White to play and mate in three. Mates don't tend to crop up in endgames but here the black king is perilously short of squares.

6   Buksza-Kovacs
Hungary 1965

Black to play and mate in four. Black would like to play 1...♔h7-g6 with a view to mating with the queen on h5, but this fails to 2 ♕d6xe6+. So how to prepare it?

7   Ernst-Benjamin
Reykjavik 1990

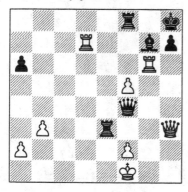

White to play and mate. White is a piece behind but there is a drastic solution. Can you spot a mating sequence?

8   Sveshnikov-Scherbakov
USSR Ch (Moscow) 1991

White to play and mate in three. CLUE: The white queen is under threat but, you've guessed it, she doesn't retreat!

9   **Bodga-Ferreira**
         Paraguay 1976

White to play and mate in three. Black is in desperate trouble but hopes that with the queens exchanged he might survive.

CLUE: The queens do get exchanged, but it doesn't help.

10   **Hort-Portisch**
         Madrid 1973

White to play and force mate. This is a well-known teaser. The first couple of moves are easy but the third move is much more subtle.

CLUE: There is another mating square besides h7.

11   **Fedoruk-Shilov**
         Leningrad 1979

White to play and mate in three. White has some heavy artillery lined up against the black king, but how to finish it off?

CLUE: Once again the lady is the sacrificial lamb.

12   **Norwood-Marsh**
         Walsall 1992

White to play and force mate. Every so often one has the chance to be frightfully artistic. Here is mine, and for once I didn't miss it.

CLUE: I didn't have one, so neither will you.

13   **Colberg-Leutloff**
Wilhelmshaven Ch 1989

White to play and mate in three. White already has a promising attack but the next move adds poetry to the position.

14   **Topalov-Shirov**
Linares 1994

Black to play and mate in three. If you are ever about to be mated by Shirov, just relax and enjoy it – he won't miss it.

CLUE: Remember how well the queen and knight work together.

15   **A. Petrosian-Glek**
USSR Cht (Azov) 1991

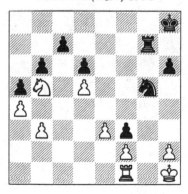

Black to play and force mate. An easy one to spot.

16   **Malaniuk-Danielsen**
Espergærde 1992

White to play and force mate. Giving a check on h8 allows the king to run and Black can limp on. What is needed is a little sacrifice to put the nail in the coffin.

17 L.B.Hansen-Mortensen
Vejle 1994

White to play and force mate in three.
CLUE: By now you shouldn't be needing any.

18   Jansa-Spiridonov
Yugoslavia 1976

White to play and mate in three. When you're material behind, why start counting?

19   Faurnoville-NN
Namur 1967

White must stop the black king from escaping via f8 and e7 and force mate. How?

20   Arkhipov-Zaitsev
Moscow 1992

Black to play and force mate in three.
CLUE: The mating net is already in place; you just have to fiddle it.

21   **Böhnisch-Uhlmann**
Leipzig 1989

Black to play and force mate in three.

22   **Izeta-Hebden**
Geneva 1988

Black to play and force mate in three. Here Mark Hebden has already sacrificed his lady, but it was well worth the investment.

23   **Zier-Formum**
W.Germany 1978

White to play and force mate. Black is a long way ahead in material and seems to be able to flee to e7. What is wrong with this reasoning?

24   **Ed. Lasker-Thomas**
London (blitz game) 1910

White to play and force mate. White has some favourable options, but we must admire the one chosen by Lasker.
CLUE: White to play and mate the black king on g1!

25   **D. Byrne-Fischer**
New York 1956

Black to play and force mate.

26   **Short-Mestel**
British Ch (Swansea) 1987

White to play and mate in three.

27   **Ljubojević-Georgiev**
Thessaloniki OL 1988

Black to play and force mate in four.

28   **Mandel-Kurze**
Berlin 1968

Black to play and force mate.

29   Nunn-Portisch
Reykjavik 1988

In this position the talented English Grandmaster Dr. John Nunn found a forced mate in four.

30   Antoniuk-Zak
Viljandi 1978

Black to play and win. Some boring players might just enjoy being a pawn ahead in this position, but once again honour calls.

31   Dreev-Agnos
Arnhem 1989

Here the young English player Demetrios Agnos is a rook and a piece up, which he hopes will be enough compensation for the queen.
How did the Russian GM put him out of his misery?

32   Short-Timman
Tilburg 1991

Here, Shorty is to play. This is not a forced mating sequence, but if Black avoids mate he incurs heavy material losses.

33   Burgess-Anderson
London Lloyds Bank 1985

White to play and mate in six.
CLUE: Think about where you can drive the black king, and then about how you can remove a key defender.

34   Chekhover-Kasparian
Erevan 1936

Here we see the endgame study king Kasparian in action. He has already dragged the white king all the way up the board. Your task is only to round it off: Black to play and force mate.

35   Barle-Jelen
Portorož 1979

Black to play and mate in five.
CLUE: You have to find one sensational decoy sacrifice.

36   Spielmann-Lisitsyn
Moscow 1935

White to play and mate in four.
CLUE: It's almost a smothered mate.

37	**Mecking-Rocha**
	1964

White to play and mate in three.

38	**Aitken-Pein**
	1962

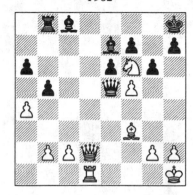

White to play and force mate.

39	**Rozenberg-Skuya**
	USSR 1962

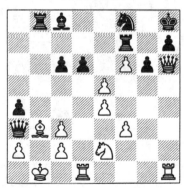

A crazy position, and a violent mate in four. White to play.

40	**Nevednichy-Marin**
	Bucharest 1994

White to play and force mate.
CLUE: A queen and knight are a powerful attacking force.

41   **Szalai-Haveland**
Drammen 1994

White to play and force mate.
CLUE: You don't have to start with a violent move.

42   **Burgess-Bank Friis**
Bellinge 1991

Black has just played ...♘f8-d7, trying to drive back White's aggressively placed forces, but this has exactly the opposite effect. White to play and win.
CLUE: Think mid-board mates!

43   **Mikenas-Bronstein**
1965

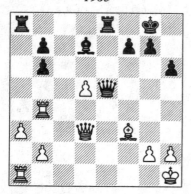

One of the classic back-rankers. Black to play and win.
CLUE: You need to overload three of White's pieces with one move!

Solutions

(1)

    1 ...   **♛d2xc1+**

        0-1

There will follow 2 ♗e3xc1 ♖d8-d1+ 3 ♘c3xd1 ♖e8-e1#.

(2)

    1 ♛f4xf7+!!   **♚g8xf7**

    2 ♗h3-e6+   **♚f7-f6**

    3 e4-e5+!   **♚f6xe5**

3...♘d7xe5 and 3...d6xe5 are both met by 4 ♘c3-e4#.

    4 ♖h1-d1!!

Threatening 5 f2-f4+ ♚e5-f6 6 ♘c3-e4#.

    4 ...   **♚e5-f6**

4...g6-g5 doesn't help because of 5 ♗h6xg5 and Black is helpless to prevent f2-f4#.

    5 ♘c3-e4+   **♚f6-e5**

    6 ♗h6-f4+!   **♚e5xe4**

    7 f2-f3#

(3)

    1 ...   **♛h6-h3+**

    2 ♚g2-h1   **♛h3xh2+**

and mate next move.

(4)

    1 ...   **♗e3-g1+**

    2 ♚h2-h1   **♗g1-f2+**

    3 ♚h1-h2   **♗f2-g3#**

(5)

    1 g3-g4+!   **♚h5xh4**

    2 ♚f2-g2!   **1-0**

Black cannot stop 3 ♘e7-f5#.

(6)

    1 ...   **♗g7-f6+!**

        0-1

The finish is 2 e5xf6 ♚h7-g6 3 g3-g4 ♛d1-e1+ and mate next move.

(7)

    1 ♛h3xh7+!   **♚h8xh7**

    2 ♖g6xg7+   **1-0**

The reasons for Black's capitulation were: 2...♚h7-h8 3 ♖g7-h7+ ♚h8-g8 4 ♖d7-g7# and 2...♚h7-h6 3 ♖g7-g6+ ♚h6-h5 4 ♖d7-h7+ ♛f4-h6 5 ♖h7xh6#.

(8)

    1 ♛e5-g7+!   **1-0**

A beautiful geometric mate will follow: 1...♚g8xg7 2 ♘d4-f5+ ♚g7-g8 3 ♘f5-h6#.

(9)
    1   ♘e4-f6+!   g7xf6
1...♘d7xf6 2 ♖d1-d8#.
    2   ♕e5xe6+   f7xe6
    3   ♗e2-h5#

(10)
    1   ♖b4-g4+!   f5xg4

    2   ♕f6-g5+   ♔g8-h8
    3   ♕g5-h6!   1-0
Black cannot stop the twin threats
of 4 ♕h6xh7# and 4 ♕h6xf8#.

(11)
    1   ♕h3-h8+!   1-0
Black had no wish to see any
more: 1...♔g8xh8 2 ♖f1-f8+ ♔h8-
h7 (2...♕e6-g8 3 ♖g4-h4#) 3 ♖g4-
h4#.

(12)
    1   ♕e4xc6+!   ♔b7xc6
    2   ♘f3xd4++   ♔c6-b6
    3   ♖e1-b1+   ♔b6-a6
3...♔b6-a5 4 ♗f4-d2+ ♔a5-a4 5
♗g2-c6+.
    4   ♗g2-b7+   ♔a6-a5
    5   ♗f4-d2+   ♔a5-a4

    6   ♗b7-c6+   ♔a4xa3

    7   ♗d2-c1+   ♔a3-a2
    8   ♖b1-b2+   ♔a2-a1
    9   ♘d4-c2#

(13)
    1   ♕e6-h6!   1-0
White threatens 2 ♕h6xh7#, and
will meet 1...g7xh6 with 2 ♖c7xh7+
♔h8-g8 3 ♘g4xh6#.

(14)
    1   ...   ♘g5-h3+
               0-1
There are two possible mates: 2
g2xh3 ♕h4-f2+ 3 ♔g1-h1 ♘e4-g3#
and 2 ♔g1-h2 ♘h3-f2+ 3 ♔h2-g1
♕h4-h1#.

(15)
    1   ...   ♘g5-h3!
               0-1
Black's idea is 2...♖g7-g1+ 3
♖f1xg1 ♘h3xf2#.

(16)
    1   ♖c1xc7!!   1-0
Intending either 2 ♖c7xf7 or 2

♛h7-h8#. If Black responds by playing 1...♝d6xc7, 2 ♝b2-a3+ ♖e8-e7 3 ♛h7-h8# rounds off nicely.

(17)
    1 ♛d3xh7+! 1-0

1...♚h8xh7 would be answered by 2 ♝f7-g8+ ♚h7-h8 3 ♖a7-h7#.

(18)
    1 ♖f1-f8+   ♚g8xf8
    2 ♛d4-h8+ ♚f8-f7
    3 ♖e1-f1#

(19)
    1 ♛f4-f6!   1-0

White intends to play 2 ♖h3-h8+ ♝g7xh8 3 ♖h1xh8#, and answer 1...♝g7xf6 with 2 e5xf6 followed by 3 ♖h3-h8#.

(20)
    1 ...   ♛g6xe4+
    2 ♖e1xe4   ♖f8-f1+
               0-1

It is mate next move.

(21)
    1 ...   ♖a8xa2+!
    2 ♚a1xa2   ♖e8-a8+
    3 ♚a2-b3   ♖a8-a3#

(22)
    1 ...   ♝f5-h3+
    2 ♚g2-h1   ♝h3-f1+
    3 ♖e2-h2   ♖h4xh2#

(23)
    1 ♖b3-h3   ♚g8-f8

Now White takes away the flight square.

(24)
    2 ♛h4xf6   ♞c6-e7
    3 ♛f6-h6+ 1-0

The black king must return to its grave.

(24)
    1 ♛h5xh7+ ♚g8xh7
    2 ♞e4xf6++ ♚h7-h6
    3 ♞e5-g4+ ♚h6-g5
    4 h2-h4+   ♚g5-f4
    5 g2-g3+   ♚f4-f3
    6 ♝d3-e2+ ♚f3-g2
    7 ♖h1-h2+ ♚g2-g1
    8 ♚e1-d2#

My only quibble is that 8 0-0-0# would have been aesthetically more pleasing.

(25)
    1 ...   ♞e4-g3+
    2 ♚f1-e1   ♝c5-b4+
    3 ♚e1-d1   ♝d5-b3+
    4 ♚d1-c1   ♞g3-e2+
    5 ♚c1-b1   ♞e2-c3+
    6 ♚b1-c1   ♖a2-c2#

(26)
    1 ♖g1xg6+ f7xg6
    2 ♝h3xe6+ ♖c7-f7
    3 ♛h6-g7#

(27)
    1 ...   ♞f5-e7+
    2 ♚g8-h8   ♚g6-h6

2...♞e6-d8 and 2...♞e6-f8 are equally effective.
    3 f4-f5   ♞e6-g5

The knight can also move to f8, d8 or f4; in all cases Black cannot avoid mate next move.
    4 f5-f6   ♞g5-f7#

(28)

1	...	♗g7xe5+
2	♔d4xe5	♕e7-c7+
3	♔e5-f6	

3 ♔e5-d4 ♕c7-g7#.

3	...	♕c7-g7+
4	♔f6-g5	♕g7-e5+
	0-1	

White cannot avoid mate next move.

(29)

1	♕h6xh7+	♔h8xh7
2	♖e4-h4+	♔h7-g7
3	♗c1-h6+	♔g7-h7
4	♗h6-f8#	

(30)

1	...	♕d7-d1+!

One starts to feel sorry for the poor old royal lady. Still, *'Dulce et decorum est...'*

2	♘e3xd1

Black wins easily after 2 ♘e3-f1 ♖e7-e1.

2	...	♖e7-e1+
	0-1	

In view of the finish 3 ♔g1-h2 ♖e1-h1#.

(31)

1	♘f7xd6+

If the knight is captured, White intends 2 ♕d1-h5+ ♔e8-f8 3 ♕h5-f7#.

2	...	♔e8-f8
3	♕d1-h5	**1-0**

(32)

1	♔h2-g3	♖c8-e8
2	♔g3-f4	♗b7-c8

Just a little more help is needed by the queen.

3	♔f4-g5	**1-0**

White will play 4 ♔g5-h6 followed by 5 ♕f6-g7#.

(33)

1	♖a1-c1+!!

1 ♕f7-c4+ ♔c6-d7 2 ♕c4-d5+ ♔d7-e7 3 ♕d5-d6+ ♔e7-f7 4 ♕d6-f6+ ♔f7-g8 gives White no instant mate.

1	...	♗h6xc1

After 1...♔c6xb5 White mates with obvious moves, for example 2 ♕f7xb7+ ♔b5-a5 3 b2-b4+ ♔a5-a4 4 ♕b7-a6+ ♔a4xb4 5 ♖c1–b1#.

2	♕f7-c4+	♔c6-d7
3	♕c4-d5+	♔d7-e7
4	♕d5-d6+	

Or 4 ♕d5-e5+.

4	...	♔e7-f7
5	♕d6-f6+	♔f7-g8
6	♕f6-g7#	

Now we see why the bishop was decoyed from h6.

(34)

1	...	♕g4-c8+
2	♔e8-e7	♕c8-c7+
3	♔e7-e8	

3 ♔e7-f6 ♔g8-f8 4 ♔f6xg5 ♕c7-g3+ 5 ♔g5-f6 ♕g3-f4+ and mate next move.

4	...	♘g5-e6
5	♖c1–d1	♘e6-g7#

(35)

1	...	♘f3-e1+
2	♔h1–g1	♕d5-h1+!!
3	♔g1xh1	♖f8-f1+

4	♕g3-g1	♗d7-c6+
5	♖e2-g2	♗c6xg2#

You don't get mating positions like that every day!

(36)

1	♘d6-f5+!	♔g7-g8

1...g6xf5 2 ♕f4-g5#.

2	♕f4-h6!	♘f6-h5
3	♕h6-g7+!	

Of course, we've seen this idea before, but it's a little harder to see in a less familiar setting.

3	...	♘h5xg7
4	♘f5-h6#	

(37)

1	♖a1-b1+	♔b8-a7
2	♕d1-d4+!	♕c3xd4
3	♘e5xc6#	

(38)

1	♕d2-h6	♕e5xf6
2	♖d1-d8+	♗e7xd8
3	♕h6-f8#	

(39)

1	♕h6xf8+	♖f7xf8
2	♖h1xh7+	♔h8xh7
3	♖d1-h1+	♗c8-h3
4	♖h1xh3#	

(40)

1	♖h3xh5!	g6xh5
2	♕f4-g5+	♘e5-g6

3	♖f1xf7+!	♔g7xf7
4	♕g5-f6+	1–0

In view of 4...♔f7-g8 5 ♕f6xg6+ ♔g8-h8 6 ♘d5-f6 ♖e8xe7 7 ♕g6-h6+ ♖e7-h7 8 ♕h6xh7#.

(41)

1	♕e3-g5!!	♔g8xf7
2	♗d3xg6+	♔f7-g8

3 &g6-h5+   &g8-f8
3...&g8-h7 4 ♕g5-g6+ &h7-h8 5 ♕g6-f6+ followed by a bishop check will mate.

4 ♕g5-f6+   &f8-g8
5 &h5-f7+   &g8-f8
6 &f7xe6#

(42)

1 ♘e5xf7!   &g8xf7

Black has little choice, as he is otherwise material down and facing a winning attack. However, there is now a thunderbolt:

2 ♕b3xe6+!

Only one exclamation mark, because it's relatively simple to calculate.

2 ...   &f7xe6

After 2...&f7-e8 3 ♘e4-d6+ mate is forced anyway.

3 ♘e4-d6+   ♘d7-e5
4 &c2-f5+

A slightly more cruel line than 4 ♖e1xe5+ &e6-d7 5 &c2-f5#.

4 ...   &e6-d5

5 ♖e1xe5#

Not a good place for a king.

(43)

1 ...   ♖a8xa3!
        0–1

White loses his queen or his king.

4 Combinations

'Where force is necessary, then it must be applied boldly, decisively and completely. But one must know the limitations of force; one must know when to blend force with a manoeuvre, a blow with an agreement.'
Leon Trotsky

The tactical themes behind combinations

For those who want to improve their tactical play, this is the chapter with a little meat. In the first three chapters we were concerned solely with a rather simple aim: checkmate. Sadly, real-life chess is much less clear-cut. In most cases you will not have the chance to force checkmate, but tactics which can result in decisive material gain continually crop up. You must hone your ability to recognise such positions, and familiarise yourself with recurring tactical themes.

What exactly do we mean by tactical themes? The most basic tactics revolve around pins, forks, skewers, discovered attacks, etc. But there is now a host of sophisticated jargon to describe more advanced themes. Before getting down to the academia, let us look at this simple position.

Prokhorovich-Ravinsky
USSR 1958

Black is to move. This position looks fairly tranquil. The material is level. The first thing to notice is that Black has a check with 1...♛c7-b6+ but after 2 ♔g1-h1 the white king is quite safe. But on further reflection you should start to realize the position is quite dynamic; why?

White is in a *Pin*, since the queen on c2 is undefended. Our first reaction might be to try 1...♘d5-e7 but White could reply with just 2 ♗c6-e4. So are there any other ways to exploit the pin? This is where a degree of imagination is required. My own method when I'm looking for tactics is to try to spot the ideal situation that I'd like to be in, and then work back to see if there is a route to it. Many times there won't be, but every so often there is pay-back...

In this position I would say to myself: 'I want to exploit the pin and win the bishop, but if I just attack it, it will move to defend the queen. Ideally, I'd like to hit both the bishop and the queen, so is a fork possible? A knight on b4 would be ideal, but a pawn is in the way, so...'

1 ...   b4-b3

This is termed *Clearance*, for obvious reasons. We are happy to sacrifice the pawn to get it out of the way. Clearance is one of the most important tactical themes.

If White captures the pawn with the queen, then the queen would be abandoning the defence of the otherwise unprotected bishop. That would be a *Decoy* – another tactical theme. So White must play:

2 a2xb3

but after

2 ...   ♘d5-b4

White will lose a piece, since the queen and bishop are *Forked*.

So here we have an innocent looking position with a whole host of tactical themes: *Pin*, *Fork*, *Clearance* and *Decoy*. Personally, I've never felt the need to memorize all the terms. The trick is to see what you want to happen and then learn to fiddle it so that it does.

Let's consider another position, slightly more advanced.

Black to move. White has rook for knight but Black's extra pawns give him a powerful position. Black's next move forces immediate resignation in any case.

Marache-Morphy
New York 1857

This position is much more dynamic. Black has knights in the centre of the board and a menacing passed pawn, but there are also more subtle observations to be made. The white queen is undefended. If the black knight weren't blocking the way the queen could just take it. Already the alarm bells should be ringing. If the white king were on h1, then just 1...♘f5-g3+ would win immediately. Any way to get it there?

Sadly, 1...♘d4-e2+ doesn't work because the knight is just grabbed by the queen. Let's make more observations. The white king is well protected by pawns, but only has one escape square. In fact, 1...♘f5-g3 would cut off that escape square. Then all we would need is a check and it would be mate...

So

1 ...   ♘f5-g3
2 ♕e4xg6

Any other move would lose the queen.

2 ...   ♘d4-e2#

Again, there are a great many tactical themes in operation. The trick is not to look for just one theme but to be trying to see them all working together. That is why I like to describe the process as 'fiddling'. Nevertheless, just to ensure familiarity with the main tactical themes, I have set a series of puzzles on each in turn. Since you will be told which theme is involved, your task here should be far easier than later in the chapter, where you are given no such clues.

a) *Clearance*

This is perhaps the easiest concept. You want to move a piece to a powerful square. The snag is that one of your own pieces is in the way; i.e. occupying the square itself or blocking your route to it. The laws of chess state that you cannot move through your own men, so what to do?

If you move the blocking piece to any old square, he will have time to defend against your threat. The solution is to sacrifice the obstructing piece so that your opponent has to take it, and then you can play your move.

Needless to say, you have to ensure that the rewards outweigh the material sacrificed!

Here Tal, the famous tactician, is playing White. He already has a good position but his next move compelled immediate resignation. What was it?

1   **Tal-Parma**
       Bled 1961

In the famous example just below, White, to move, has already sacrificed two pieces. What move would he like to play and how does he get to play it?

2   **Roneat-Reicher**
       Germany 1950

b) *Decoy*

This is my own favourite tactical theme. The decoy is when you sacrifice in order to force your opponent to a certain square. There is another tactical theme called *Distraction* although I'm still at a loss to figure out what the difference is between the two.

This concept is best illustrated with a diagram.

Belenky-Pirogov
Moscow 1958

Black is to move and there is no doubt that White's position is critical because of his bad king position. The black queen would like to give checkmate on a square such as g2 or h5. Sadly White has them both guarded, so what to do?

1 ...   Ee8-e1

The rook is a small price to pay for checkmate; this occurs in three variations: after 2 ♕d1xe1 ♕d5-h5#, 2 ♖g1xe1 ♕d5-g2# or 2 ♕d1-g4 ♕d5-h1+ 3 ♖g1xh1 ♖e1xh1#. The only way for White to avoid immediate mate is by playing 2 c3-c4 but after 2...♖e1xg1 3 c4xd5 ♖g1xd1 it's hopeless for White.

I suppose this is an example of *Distraction* since we are distracting more than one piece rather than decoying a specific piece.

3   A.N. Other-Philipp
Halle 1912

'Necessity is the mother of invention.' Here Black is in such desperate straits that you need to find something drastic to stay alive. The first move is obvious when you consider there are no real alternatives. How did Black turn the tables and force checkmate?

4   Morphy-Maurian
New Orleans 1864

Here Paul Morphy, one of the greatest ever players, is to move. On paper he is behind in material. Not for long; what did he play?

CLUE: There are two key tactical points on which to focus. The first is that the queen and king are aligned on the same file; ideally we'd like to pin them with the rook. Secondly, were the queen not defending the d5-square we would have a mating net after 1 ♕b7-d5+ ♚d8-e8 2 ♕d5-e6+ ♚e8-d8 3 ♕e6-e7. How to exploit both these factors?

c) *Interference*

This is another self-explanatory tactical theme. One places a piece, usually as a sacrifice, in such a way so that when captured it will destroy the co-ordination of the enemy pieces. As usual, the concept is best explained with a diagram.

White is far behind in material but there are tactics around to save the day. White, to move, would like to play 1 ♕e2-h2+ with a view to mating on h7. The drawback is that Black would just play 1...♕d6xh2+ with a winning endgame; i.e. Black's control of h2 prevents the combination which would otherwise win.

So the trick is to interfere with Black's line of communication so that h2 is no longer covered. 1 ♘f3-e5 would be one way of doing this, but 1 ♗c3-e5 is a far more powerful solution. Not only is White interfering, but he is doing so while attacking a major piece. Black is now faced with a rather dismal dilemma: retreat the queen and allow mate with 2 ♕e2-h2+ and 3 ♕h2-h7 or play 1...♕d6xe5. Either way Black is lost.

5

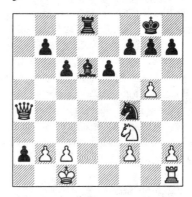

Here Black has sacrificed a queen but it appears that the attack is fizzling out. One's first instinct is to play 1...♘f4-e2+ but after 2 ♚c1-d2 there are no useful discovered checks. It would also be nice to promote the a-pawn but the queen has it covered. Thinking along the lines of interference, how can Black force a win?

In the diagram at the top of the next page, Black is a pawn down but his control of the h-file offers a whiff of compensation. The rather blunt

6   **Kreutzaller-Leopold**
        Zittau 1973

Mukhin-Chechalian
1972

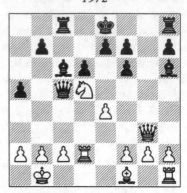

1...♖f6-h6 fails to 2 ♖c1-c7+ when the black king is embarrassed;, for example 2...♔g7-f8 3 ♖c7-c8+ takes a pair of rooks off, while 2...♔g7-f6 3 ♖c7-f7+ ♔f6-g5 4 ♖f7-g7+ either forces perpetual check or drives Black's king onto the h-file, blocking the attack. Black to play and win.

CLUE: Black's play down the h-file is well worth a pawn; it's even worth a piece!

d) *Intermezzo*

This is an intermediate move, or as the Germans say, a *zwischenzug*. Perhaps the easiest definition is the 'in-between' move, but I think intermezzo sounds nicer. An intermezzo occurs when one player plays a move (such as a capture) and expects an obvious reply (e.g. a recapture); instead the other player throws a move in between which radically alters the situation. The following diagram provides an illustration.

Here Black has just hit the rook with ...♗h6. Obviously 1 ♕g3-h3,

attacking the rook and bishop, is the first move that Black would have considered. He probably assumed that 1...♗c6xd5 would win easily after 2 e4xd5 ♗h6xd2. This is a common failing of the chess mind. We tend to analyse moves in pairs, forgetting that even the most obvious replies are not necessarily forced.

1   ♕g3-h3   ♗c6xd5

However, White is under no obligation to recapture.

2   ♗f1-b5+

A devastating 'in-between' move.

2   ...   ♔e8-f8

If 2...♔e8-d8, 3 ♕h3-d7 is mate.

3   ♕h3xh6+

An intermezzo can be several moves deep.

3   ...   ♔f8-g8
4   e4xd5

White was finally ready to recapture. After 4...♕c5xb5, 5 ♖d2-d3 with the threat of 6 ♖d3-g3+ is devastating.

In the next diagram, White is to move. Black must have been aware

7   **Jung-Rogman**
       1937

of possible danger in view of the f6-pawn. Doubtless he calculated 1 ♕e3-h6 ♕c7-c5+ and after the king moves to h1, the queen can retreat to the defensive square f8, stopping the mate on g7. This reasoning is logical but flawed; why?

8   **Alekhine-Levenfish**
       St. Petersburg 1914

Alekhine, White to move, has his queen under attack. Despite the backward development of his queen-side, he has a very powerful inter-mezzo.

e) *Mating Positions*

A whole host of tactical themes revolve around positions in which checkmate is possible. The most basic example is the back rank mate:-

You might expect this dull end-game position to end in a draw. But any experienced player would focus on Black's vulnerable back rank. A simple decoy is all that is needed.

     1 ♖c1-d1

Black will suffer heavy material loss or be mated.

9   **Bronstein-Keres**
       Budapest 1950

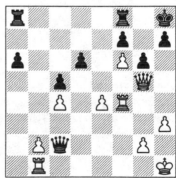

This is a classic 'checkmate position' with the pawn on f6 supporting a mate on g7. The beauty of this puzzle is that in seeking to avoid one mating threat, Black must walk into another mating position. White to play and win.

10 Cochrane-Staunton
London 1942

Black could capture the knight with 1...♘g5xe6, but after 2 ♕d3xd5 White, who is attacking c4, d6 and e6, would be winning back the piece with interest. Focus instead on the vulnerable squares around the white king.

Solutions

(1)

1 ♕e6xf5

After the queen is recaptured White can play 2 ♘g5-e6+ forking the queen and king.

(2)

1 ♕h6-e6+

Black is obliged to capture the queen by 1...♘f8xe6 or 1...♗c8xe6. Either way it makes no difference; White plays 2 ♘f5-h6#. Note that e6 was the only good square on which to give up the queen; anywhere else would have broken the mating net around the black king.

(3)

1 ...   ♖g1-g4+
2 ♔h4xg4

Forced because the h-pawn is pinned.

2 ...   ♕h1-g2+
3 ♔g4-h4   g6-g5+
4 f4xg5   ♕g2xg5#

(4)

1 ♖e1-e2

Brilliant. If 1...♕d3xe2 then 2 ♕b7-d5+ forcing mate in two more moves – but what else can Black do? The king cannot move since the c8-rook would be lost. 1...♕d3-d1+ 2 ♔g1-f2 achieves nothing. There is no way of countering the threat of 2 ♖e2-d2.

(5)

1 ...   ♗d6-a3

There is no way to cope with both threats. 2 ♕a4xa3 is met by 2...♘f4-e2#. Otherwise 2...a2-a1=♕+ wins.

(6)

1 ...   ♘e4-c3
2 f2-f4

Or 2 b2xc3 ♖f6-h6 3 f2-f3 g4-g3 and Black will mate on h1.

2 ...   g4-g3

3 Rc1xc3   b4xc3
4 Rf1-f3   c3xb2
5 Rf3xg3+   ♔g7-f8

and Black is winning.

(7)

1 ♕e3-h6   ♕c7-c5+
2 Rd1-d4

This is a particularly pleasing in-between move. After 2...♕c5xd4+ 3 ♔g1-h1 there is no way to guard against the checkmate on g7, while after 2...♕c5-f8 3 ♕h6xf8+, followed by 4 Rd4xb4, White emerges a full piece ahead.

(8)

1 ♘g5xf7   Rf8xf7
2 ♕e2-c4

White is now winning a decisive quanitiy of material.

2 ...   ♗g4-h5
3 ♕c4xc6

(9)

1 ♕g5-h6

The rook on c1 is of no importance in the grand scheme of things.

1 ...   ♕c2xb1+
2 ♔h1-h2   Rf8-g8
3 ♕h6xh7+   ♔h8xh7
4 Rf4-h4#

(10)

1 ...   ♘g5xh3+
2 g2xh3   Rc4-g4+
3 h3xg4   ♕h4-h2#

Now you are on your own....

11 Bogoljubow-Ed. Lasker
New York 1924

Opposite-coloured bishop endings have a frustrating tendency to end in a draw. White could play 1 ♔d4-c5, but there is a way to bring about a speedier conclusion. What is it?

12 Konstantinopolsky – Ilyin-Zhenevsky
Leningrad 1936

Here Black, to move, has an advanced pawn on b3, but its path is currently blocked. Is there any way to remedy this situation?

13	**Lukacs-Krizsany**
	Kecskemet 1991

In this position Black continued 1...♖f8-d8 to reinforce the knight on d5. Why was this not an adequate solution?

14	**Lautier-Hertneck**
	Tilburg 1992

Here Black played 1...♖e2-e1; how did White exploit the overworked black queen?

15	**Krasenkov-Shvedchikov**
	Moscow 1992

Black advanced his pawn with 1...b5-b4; why was this a mistake?

16	**Heine Nielsen-Vogt**
	Valby 1991

White is an exchange up, but in an awkward pin. He decides to reinforce his g4 pawn with 1 h2-h3. Does Black then have anything better than regaining his material?

17 **Short-Bareev**
Tilburg 1991

Here Britain's former number one, Nigel Short, smiled to himself after 1...♘c6xe5. How did he punish this greedy pawn-snatch?

18 **Kasparov-Timman**
Tilburg 1991

Black now continued 1...♗c8xa6?. How did Kasparov now encourage Timman to resign?

19 **Hort-Kasparov**
Cologne 1988

Black to play and win.

20 **Kiselev-Tal**
USSR Ch (Moscow) 1991

In this position Mikhail Tal, who was World Champion 1960-61, continued 1...♖c3-b3?. What was White's brilliant response?

21   **Farago-Magomedov**
Ljubljana Iskra 1992

1   ♔g1-h1??
The white queen protects g2, so how should Black reply?

22 **Van der Sterren-Van Mil**
Dutch Ch 1992

Black played 1...♗d7-b5?. Why is this a mistake?

23   **Tal-Bilek**
Miskolc 1963

White to play and win.

24   **Fischer-Schweber**
Buenos Aires 1970

The white bishop is attacked, but moving it is not a thrilling prospect. Bobby Fischer found a more dramatic response; what was it? CLUE: The pin along the h2-b8 diagonal could be worth a queen!

25 **Goglidze-Kasparian**
USSR 1934

How can White make progress in this position, since Black's pieces defend each other well?

CLUE: After 1 g3-g4 ♖h2-h3+ 2 ♔f3-f4 ♖h3-h4, Black's defence may not be as solid as it looks.

26 **Amos-Norwood**
Toronto 1985

Black to play and win.

27 **S. Saeed-Norwood**
London 1984

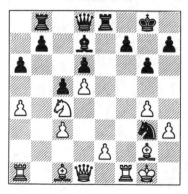

Black to play and justify his piece sacrifice.

28 **Ortueta-Sanz**
Madrid 1934

Always be on the look-out when pawns are close to the end of the board! Here Black, to play, has a brilliant move to exploit this factor, but there are lots of twists and turns in this one.

29 Ragozin-Levenfish
Moscow 1935

Here White played 1 ♔e1-d1, allowing Black a forced mate after 1...♖c2xc1+ 2 ♔d1xc1 ♕a5xa3+. What saving throw did White overlook?

30 Geller-Notaros
Novi Sad 1978

White is a rook down, but there is a brilliant route to a draw.
CLUE: This is a similar theme to the last puzzle.

31 Anand-Kamsky
Las Palmas PCA Ct (11) 1995

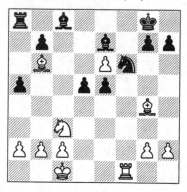

The above position could have arisen in the decisive game of the match from which Anand qualified to play against Kasparov. Anand (to move) had a fantastic combination in mind.

32 Levitt-Mortazavi
London Lloyds Bank Masters 1992

White, to play, notices that Black has weakened his kingside with a series of pawn moves. The combination begins now but the real point of it is not seen until the end.

33 **Tarrasch-Alekhine**
Pistyan 1922

Black to play and win.

34 **Cifuentes-Zviagintsev**
Wijk aan Zee 1995

Here Black has already sacrificed a rook to reach the above diagram. The position looks good for Black but perhaps it is slightly surprising that he can force mate in five!

35 **Tal-Olafsson**
Las Palmas 1975

Black to play and win.
CLUE: White's bank rank is the key to the solution.

36 **Ljubojević-Anand**
Buenos Aires 1994

In time trouble, White played 1 ♕f5-g5?. However, both players missed White's winning possibility, which was later found by the chess-playing software *Genius 3*.

Solutions

(11)

1	♗d8xg5	♔f5xg5
2	d5-d6	♔g5-f6
3	d6-d7	♗e8xd7
4	e6xd7	♔f6-e7
5	♔d4-c5	a7-a6
6	♔c5-b6	1-0

(12)

1	...	♗d6xa3
2	b2xa3	b3-b2
3	♘c6-b4	

3 ♖d1-b1 loses to the continuation 3...♖a4-c4.

3	...	♖a4xa3
4	♘b4-c2	♖a3-c3

The white pieces cannot co-ordinate to prevent the advance of the b-pawn. Note that Black's tactics where made possible by the added threats of a back-rank mate. White therefore resigned.

(13)

Because of...

2	♖c5xd5!	♘f6xd5
3	♗a2xd5	♕d7xd5
4	♖e1-e8+	♔g8-h7
5	♕f3xd5	♖d8xd5
6	♖e8xc8	1-0

(14)

2	♖f4xf6!	♖e1xf1+
3	♗g2xf1	1-0

Black is lost after 3...♕e5xf6 4 ♕f7xf6 g7xf6 5 ♗f1-d3+.

(15)

White can win by utilising multiple pins:

2	♘c3-a4	♕b6-a5
3	♘a4xc5	♗e7xc5

3...♖c7xc5 4 ♗e3xc5 ♗e7xc5 5 ♖d1-d7 wins for White. The pinned f-pawn is lost and with it the king.

4 ♕f4-e5!

A pin along the rank and file!

4	...	♖f8-c8

Other lines are no better: 4...♗c5-b6 5 ♕e5xa5 ♗b6xa5 6 ♖c1xc7 ♗a5xc7 7 ♖d1-d7 or 4...♗c5xe3 5 ♕e5xa5 ♖c7xc1 6 ♖d1xc1 ♗e3xc1 7 ♕a5-c7.

5	♖c1xc5!!	♖c7xc5
6	♗b3xf7+!	1-0

The final blow: after the king takes the bishop, the rook comes to the seventh rank. Mate follows.

(16)
Yes!

1 ... ♖f4xe4

There's no need to cash in yet as the rook isn't going anywhere.

2 ♖e1xe4 ♕c7-c1+
3 ♔g1-h2

If 3 ♔g1-f2, then 3...♕c1-c2+ is decisive.

3 ... ♗b7-d5!

Not 3...♕c1-b1?? as after 4 ♖e4-e1! ♕b1xe1 5 ♕g2xb7+ White has the advantage.

4 ♕g2-e2

What else?

4 ... ♕c1-b1

and Black wins.

(17)

2 ♘d6-f5

This is a hard move to answer. If knight grabs White's queen then 3 ♖d1xd8# follows, while there is no answer to the double threats on g7 and d8.

(18)

2 ♕e1-c1! 1-0

Black cannot stop the dual threats of ♘c6-e7+ followed by ♕c1xc7 or the simple b5xa6 winning a piece.

(19)

1 ... ♖e6xe3+!
2 ♕d3xe3

Black wins after 2 ♘f1xe3 ♕g2-g1+ 3 ♕d3-f1 ♖e8xe3+.

2 ... ♖e8xe3+
3 ♘f1xe3 ♕g2-g1+
4 ♘e3-f1 ♗g7xc3
5 ♖b1-b2

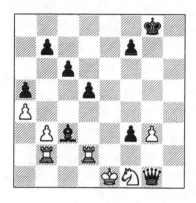

5 ... ♕g1-g2!
0-1

(20)

2 ♕b1xb3!! ♗e6xb3
3 ♖a7-a8 ♘f4-e6

If 3...♕d8-b8 then 4 ♖a8xb8+ ♘c6xb8 5 ♗e3-a7 is winning for White. Also, 3...♘c6-b8 fails to 4 ♗e3-a7 ♕d8-c7 4 ♖a8xb8+ ♔g8-h7 5 ♗f1-a6 ♕c7-c1+ 6 ♘g3-f1 winning.

4 ♗e3-b6! ♕d8-f8
5 ♖a8-c8!!

White intends simply to capture the c6-knight before returning to c8 to pick up the queen.

5 ... ♗b3-a4

5...♘c6-b8 6 ♖c8xf8+ ♗g7xf8 7 ♗b6-a7 is winning.

6 ♗f1-c4! ♗g7-f6

6...♔g8-h7 7 ♖c8xf8 ♗g7xf8 8 ♗c4xe6 f7xe6 9 ♗b6-c7 and White wins.

7 ♗c4xe6 f7xe6
8 ♖c8xf8+ ♔g8xf8
9 ♗b6-c7! 1-0

White will be a piece up.

(21)
... interpose!

1 ... &c4-e2!!
0-1

2 &c1-g1 loses after 2...&g6xg2 3 &g1xg2 &f3-f1+ 4 &g2-g1 &e2-f3+, whilst 2 &g2xf3 is refuted by 2...&e2xf3+ 3 &b2-g2 &g6xg2 (or 3...&f3xg2+ 4 &h1-g1 &g2xe4+) 4 &c1-f1 &f3xe4 5 &f1-f4 &g2xa2+ 6 &f4xe4 d5xe4, with a decisive advantage.

(22)

2 &c1-c7+ &f7-g8

If 2...&f7-f6 then White wins by 3 a2-a4! &b5xe2 4 &b1-b6+ &f6-f5 5 &c7xg.

3 &b1xb5! a6xb5
4 &a5-c6 1-0

(23)

1 &f1xf6 &f8xf6
2 &g3xe5 a4xb3
3 a2xb3

This is the really beautiful move behind the combination. White is a rook down but the pin against f6 is so powerful that there is no need to rush.

3 ... b7-b6
4 b3-b4

Another finesse, preventing the intended 4...&a6-a5, which would complicate matters. Now there is no stopping 5 &d1-f1, so Black resigned.

(24)

1 &e3xe4 &c7xg3
2 &e4xd4

The black queen is completely dominated; there is no option but to return the queen.

2 ... &g3-g4
3 &d4xg4 &d7xg4
4 &d3xg6

And with two powerful pawns for the exchange, Fischer went on to win.

(25)

1 g3-g4 &h2-h3+
2 &f3-f4 &h3-h4
3 &c5xf5 g6xf5
4 &f4xf5 1-0

There is no sensible way to avoid 5 g4-g5+ and 6 &c7xh7#.

(26)

1 ... &e8xe3
2 &f2xe3

2 &c1xe3 is also well met by 2...h7-h6 with ...&f6-g4+ to follow.

2 ... h7-h6

This is the key move. The knight cannot retreat to a sensible square, e.g. 3 &g5-f3 &f6-g4+ 4 &e3-d2 &d8-a5+ with mate to follow, or 3 &g5-e4 &d8-e7 4 &d1-c2 &a8-e8 and Black regains the knight.

3 &e3-f2

White has nothing better than to abandon the knight.

3 ... h6xg5
4 f4xg5 &f6-g4+
5 &f2-g1 &d8-b6
6 e2-e3 &a8-e8

Black has a crushing position.

(27)

1 ... &d7xg4

White cannot capture the bishop due to 2 h3xg4 ♘g3xe2+ 3 ♔g1-h2 ♕d8-h4+ 4 ♗g2-h3 ♕h4-g3+ 5 ♔h2-h1 ♕g3xh3#. However, 2 ♕d1-e1! would have given White chances to save the game.

2	♕d1-d3	♘g3xe2+
3	♔g1-h2	♘e2xc1
4	♖f1xc1	♗g4-e2
	0-1	

(28)

1	...	♖d2xb2!!
2	♘a4xb2	c4-c3

If the knight wants to stop the pawn, 3 ♘b2-d3 is the only square to cover it, but this fails to 3...c5-c4 4 ♖b7xb6 c4xd3. Two connected passed pawns on the sixth rank always beat a rook when the defender's king is far away.

3	♖b7xb6	c5-c4

This move is the real beauty. The key is to cover the d3-square so that 4...c3-c2 is threatened.

4	♖b6-b4	a7-a5

Poetry. After 5 ♖b4xc4 c3xb2 the a-pawn prevents the rook covering on b4.

5	♘b2-a4	a5xb4
	0-1	

There is no way to prevent 6...c3-c2 and queens.

(29)

1	♕h7xe7+	♔d7xe7
2	♖f1-f7+	♔e7-d8
3	♖f7-f8+	♔d8-d7
4	♖f8-f7+	½-½

Black cannot escape the perpetual check.

(30)

1	♕g4xh5+!!	♔h6xh5
2	g3-g4+	♔h5xg4

2...♔h5-h6 3 g4-g5+ is better for White.

3	♗d3-e2+	♔g4-f5
4	♗e2-d3+	♔f5-g4
5	♗d3-e2+	♔g4-h3
6	♗e2-f1+	½-½

With perpetual check to the black king.

(31)

1	♖f1xf6!!	g7xf6

After 1...♗e7xf6, Black faces much the same problems.

2	♘c3xd5	♔e8-f8

and now the key move:

3	♗g4-f5!!	

Black cannot move a single piece. White will simply march his king in and eventually pick up the rook on a8.

(32)

1	♖e1xe4!	d5xe4
2	♘d4xe6	♖e8xe6
3	♗f1-c4	♕d8-b6

Obviously White will regain the sacrificed material but can he get more out of the position?

4	♕c2xe4	♖a8-e8
5	♖a1-e1!	

Of course, there is no need to regain the material just yet. The pin will not run away...

5	...	♔g8-f7
6	g2-g4!	

Preventing the move ...f6-f5 as g4xf5 would net a whole rook thanks to the devastating pin.

6	...	♛b6-c6
7	♕e4xc6	b7xc6
8	♗h2-d6!!	

The star move. Black's pieces are in their optimum positions and he has nothing but pawn moves left, and shuffling his bishop from g7 to h8, so White will just bring in his king and win easily. Note that after 8...♗g7-f8 9 ♗d6xf8, Black has no good way of recapturing and thus loses a piece.

(33)

1	...	♜f7-f3!

This was a possible variation in the game.

2	♕c6xe4	

If 2 g2-g3 Black comes crashing through with 2...♗d6xg3 3 ♘f1xg3 ♜f3xg3+ 4 f2xg3 ♛g5xg3+ 5 ♔g1-h1 ♛g3xh3+ 6 ♔h1-g1 ♛h3-g3+ 7 ♔g1-h1 ♗e6-g4 8 ♗b2xg7+ ♔h8-g8+, winning.

2	...	♗e6-d5
3	♕e4-d3	

3	...	♛g5xg2+!!
4	♔g1xg2	♜f3-g3++

5	♔g2-h2	♜g3-g2++
6	♔h2-h1	♜g2-h2++
7	♔h1-g1	♜h2-h1#

(34)

1	...	♕e6-e3+!!
2	♗f4xe3	

2 ♔f3xg4 ♗b7-c8#.

2	...	♜e8xe3+
3	♔f3xg4	♗b7-c8+
4	♔g4-g5	h7-h6+!!
5	♔g5xh6	♜e3-e5!!

White cannot avert both ...♜e5-h5# and ...♗d6-f8#.

(35)

1	...	♕d6-f4!!

Black tries to divert the white queen from defending the d1-square.

2	♜c7-e7!	

An ingenious counterattack. Instead 2 ♕d2xf4 allows 2...♜d8-d1+ 3 ♘f3-e1 ♜d1xe1#.

2	...	♜e8-f8!

Black resumes his back-rank attack. White should win after either 2...♜d8xd2 3 ♜e7xe8+ ♔g8-g7 4 ♘f3xd2 or 2...♕f4xd2 3 ♜e7xe8+.

3 ♕d2-a5

If 3 ♕d2-e1 then 3...♝g4xf3 4 g2xf3 ♕f4xf3 5 ♖c2-c1 ♖d8-d4+ winning; Black also wins after 3 ♕d2-e2 ♝g4xf3 4 ♕e2xf3 ♕f4-d6+.

3 ...   ♖d8-d1+

It is possible to play 3...♕f4-g5 here with the same ideas as in the game.

4 ♘f3-e1   ♕f4-g5!

Again the key is to divert the white queen, this time from the e1-square.

5 ♕a5-b4   ♕g5xe7

The same theme but this time it is de_ , ·e.

0-1

(36)

1 ♝b3-d5!!

The black queen is now over-loaded – it cannot defend both h6 and the bishop on b7. Black's reply is forced:

1 ...   ♖d8xd5

2 ♕f5xd5!

White is winning after 2...♖d8-c8 3 ♕d5-g5! or 2...♔h8-h7 3 ♕d5xc6 ♝b7xc6 4 c3xb4.

5 Chess: A Cruel Game

This is the part where we indulge ourselves in complete, unashamed *schadenfreude*. Yes, chess is a cruel game. Only a chess player understands the meaning of true pain. There is nothing worse than losing a winning chess position. One can lose one's job, or your house could fall down. These things happen in life, and time is a healer. But losing a particularly bad chess game, that is a travesty of justice that will leave emotional scars that will never, ever heal.

In this chapter, we enjoy the pain of many a chess playing great. We flash back to great moments in history where destiny hangs on a single move – and our heroes miss them. It is such moments that humble woodpushers like ourselves should be thankful that we are not in the shoes of the demigods, whose miseries take on divine proportions. We also relish over some of the great injustices in the history of the game, and we dwell on a curious trait of the human race; the suicidal lemming-like urge.

This is not really a Chapter of puzzles, and the 'answers' (or what should have happened) are placed under the diagrams. This will make it easier for us to relish the depths of human misery.

Missed Opportunities

'Chess is one long regret'
Stephen Leacock
'The man who makes no mistakes, does not usually make anything'
Edward John Phelps 1822-1900
'It is worse than a crime; it is a blunder.'
Joseph Fouche, Duke of Otranto 1763-1820 (of the murder of Duc d'Enghien by Napoleon)

Bronstein-Botvinnik
Moscow 1951

This position is without doubt one of the great missed chances in the history of chess. Bronstein is White, to move, and it's game 6 of his World Championship match with Botvinnik, which eventually ended in a

12-12 draw (and so, under the rules of the time, Botvinnik retained the Championship). He is leading the match by a point, so two draws would secure the title. 1 ♘d8-e6+ followed by 2 ♘e6-d4 would give White an easy draw. Instead he ponders for a full forty five minutes...

1   ♔b3-c2

Black's reply must still be waking Bronstein in the night.

1   ...   ♔f4-g3

And now there is no way to stop the e2-pawn.

2   ♔c2-d1   ♔g3-f2

A couple of years ago I asked Bronstein about this game; 'Even after half a century it is still difficult to talk about it...'

Garcia-Ivkov
Havana 1965

In this position, the Yugoslavian Grandmaster, Borislav Ivkov, was coasting to an easy victory. What is more, a win would clinch first place with a round to spare in the powerful Capablanca Memorial. With two

pawns and a rook for a piece, what could possibly go wrong?

1   ...   d4-d3

2   ♗d2-c3

It never ceases to amaze how great minds can be equally ingenious at creating their own destruction. Mundane moves would have won easily for Black. It takes rare talent to play a move like 1...d4-d3.

Korchnoi and Petrosian did not like each other much, as anyone who has read Viktor's *Chess is My Life* will know well. I can just imagine Viktor 'the Terrible' thinking to himself when his adversary threw away the following dominating position; 'It couldn't have happened to a nicer guy.'

Petrosian-Korchnoi
Moscow 1963

White's first move is fairly natural, but one should always smell for rats when there are passed pawns around.

1 ♖g6xh6 f4-f3 2 ♖h6-h7+ ♔f7-g8

The next position is without doubt the stuff of tragicomedy. White to move cannot have been unhappy with his position. Rather than focusing on his extra pawns, Tomovic recalled the old maxim: 'Give a check: it might be mate.' Yes, but for whom?

Tomović-Sokolov
Belgrade 1961

1   ♖a5-e5+   ♔e3-f2
At this point White might have begun regretting giving a check. In fact there is no defence to the threat of ...♖d1–h1+. For example...2 a2-a4 ♖d1-h1+ 3 ♗g2xh1 ♘g3-f1#

A curiously large number of disasters seem to occur in queen and pawn endgames. Given that there are no knights hopping around to confuse matters, this seems rather odd. Perhaps it is the apparent simplicity of the positions that stimulates blindness. In this position Simagin correctly figured that he had achieve a winning queen and pawn endgame. His method of execution, though, was not the best...

Batuyev-Simagin
Riga 1954

**1...e3-e2?? 2 ♕g7-g1+ ♔e1-d2
3 ♕g1-c1+ ♔d2-d3 4 ♕c1-c3#**

There was a happy ending to Simagin's story, when a year later he found himself under pressure in the Soviet Championships. White is no longer winning and despite the extra pawn he should probably allow a perpetual. Instead he follows the principle 'use your king actively in the endgame'...

Borisenko-Simagin
USSR Ch 1955

1 ♔h3-g4 f7-f5+

Simagin knew full well that queen endgames were dangerous territory. His opponent resigned at this point, probably not happy with the outcome at all. Mate was coming after the moves 2 g5xf6 ♕f1-f5+ 3 ♔g4-h4 ♕h1-h5#

Mates that are Stale

'The next worse thing to a battle lost is a battle won.'
Wellington after Waterloo, 1815

He was wrong; the next worse thing to a battle lost is allowing a stalemate.

I once knew a fellow who always seemed unhappy. He never really spoke to anyone, and even though he rarely missed a tournament he didn't seem to enjoy the games. One day I saw him struggling to hold a losing position, looking miserable as ever. . Suddenly his opponent allowed a stalemate opportunity, which he immediately seized. Simultaneously his sombre face broke into the broadest grin I have ever seen.

Simple stalemates when there are very few pieces left on the board are not particularly rare. But it is quite a spectacle when a player forces a stalemate with queen and rook still on the board...

1...♖b8-b1+ 2 ♔g1-h2 ♖b1-h1+ 3 ♔h2xh1 ♘e4-g3+ 4 f2xg3

I set this position as a competition for *Telegraph* readers. Virtually

Ormos-Betotski
Budapest 1951

everyone got it right up to this point, but there is only one correct way to continue...

4...♕c2xg2+

Note that 4...♕c2-c1+ does not lead to the same conclusion. White can win by 5 ♗g4-d1 ♕b1xd1+ 6 ♔h1-h2 lifting the stalemate.

5 ♔h1xg2 and Black is left in stalemate.

These stalemates are spectacular, if unlikely to occur in real games very often. But it can be of practical benefit to bear in mind stalemate possibilities in the endgames, especially if your king has few flight squares. The next position is a prime example of a free half point thanks to the stalemate.

Schlechter-Wolff
Nuremberg 1906

1...Rc3-e3

This is a tricky little move, but White really ought to have smelt a rat. After all, Black has only one saving throw left.

2 b5-b6 Re3-e1+ 3 Rb1xe1 stalemate

It has been said that the threat of extinction concentrates the mind wonderfully. In the following position Vaisman has a dilemma: perish or find the brilliancy. Which would you choose?

1...Nh3-f2+ 2 Be3xf2 Qg4-h3+
Now 3 Bf1xh3 is stalemate, so...

3 Kh1-g1 Qh3-g4+ 4 Kg1-h2 Qg4-h3+ 5 Kh2xh3 with stalemate in any case.

Rodriguez-Vaisman
Bucharest 1974

The next position is another classic example of utilising the stalemate theme as a means of evening the score.

Tomović-Vidmar
Ljubljana 1945

1   Kc5-d6

This move is natural enough, but Black's reply isn't! White might still have won if he had played 1 Ra7-e7 instead..

1	...	Re1xe5
2	Kd6xe5	f7-f6+
3	Ke5xf6	stalemate

The next position is by far my favourite stalemate and perhaps one of the greatest swindles of all time. The aesthetic appeal lies in the number of pieces still on the board. There cannot be many stalemates that occur from a middlegame position!

Troitsky-Vogt
1896

1   ℁c1-d1

Inviting a move that Black is simply unable to resist. He could have won by means of 1...℁g6xg3+ 2 h2xg3 ♕f3xg3+ 4 ♔g1-f1 ♝d7-h3+ 5 ℁h1xh3 ♕g3xh3+ followed by ...♕h3-g4+, but to be fair, who would be thinking about stalemates with so many pieces on the board?

1   ...   ♝d7-h3
2   ℁d1xd8+   ♔c8xd8
3   ♕c2-d1+

No option other than to capture the queen.

3   ...   ♕f3xd1

De-mobilising White's last remaining piece. Black could hardly wish for a more dominating position. Sadly, things can be too good.

Stalemate

'Well played...I resign.'

'It's universal, this self-destructive urge.'
Juvenal 60-140 AD
'*Worse!* How could it be worse? ... Jehovah! Jehovah! Jehovah!'
Monty Python's *Life Of Brian* (the character in question, about to be stoned to death for blasphemy, had just been warned that by repeating Jehovah 'you are only making it worse for yourself')
'Nobody ever improved their position by resigning.'

I have always been amazed by the eagerness that many chess players have for laying down their king. As an unrepentant swindler, I find it almost offensive when players give up the game when there are plenty of tricks left. Chess is a practical struggle, played between humans (mostly) and gross blunders are inevitable among the elite as they are at the bottom. Besides, any player, however experienced, will lose some concentration when winning easily. So why rush to resign? Why not try springing a few traps, however simple? After all, once you have accepted the game as lost, it cannot really get worse.

During the Icelandic Chess Summit in 1990, I was playing for England against Scandinavia. I had been completely outplayed and my position was totally lost. It was so hopeless that my team mates, Julian Hodgson and Michael Adams had gone back to the hotel and had a beer waiting for me. But I dug in, set swindle after swindle, and somehow managed to return to some warm beer and astonished friends. At the other end of the scale I once threw away a position against Boris Gelfand that was so good that my second had gone to buy the champagne.

The first thing that I emphasise to a new pupil is that one should fight to the bitter end. OK, I do not mean playing on two rooks and a queen down against a grandmaster, but continuing the game until it is virtually inconceivable that your opponent can go wrong. Most of the players eagerly laying down their kings tend to be a long way from this point. Believe it or not, some players have spent more time trying to convince me that it was right to resign, than they spent thinking about their actual moves. Anyway, if I haven't convinced you of the merits of fighting to the last man, just take a look at

the following collection of positions....

This is perhaps the most famous example of hara-kiri on the chessboard. Black, to move, could find no way to counter the pin on the d-file. Expecting the loss of a piece, Marco played the rather uninspiring 1...Resigns. Assuming that he wasn't trying to sneak off to a hot date, what should he have played?

Von Popiel-Marco
Monte Carlo 1902

| 1 | ... | ♗d4-g1 |

Objectively a better move, since White is now losing after 2 ♔h1xg1 ♖d7xd3 3 ♗b1xd3 ♗b7xe4. Otherwise there is no good defence to the mate on h2. But then, had he found this continuation, would we still be writing about him today?

The next position is less easy to forgive, since Black is so far ahead in material that *anything* could be considered. White has just moved his queen to f6 threatening checkmate on g7, but 1...g7xf6 allows 2 ♖d3-g3

♔g8-h8 3 ♗c3xf6, with an attractive mate.

Ahues-Müller
Berlin 1920

1...♕e2-g4

Defending g7 is quite a logical solution, after all. If the pawn takes the queen, then Black just does the same, so...

2 ♖d3-g3 ♕g4xg3 3 f2xg3 g7xf6

Resignable, but not for Black.

Rudenko was a women's World Champion. I also suspect that she might have given a tremendous boost to the chauvinistic nature of the chess world. Women do not have a reputation for being the greatest fighters in chess. Sexism? Look at the next position, and ...ahem...

1   ...   b3-b2

After this move, our heroine opted for the wonderfully pessimistic **2 Resigns**. Presumably she had just considered **2 ♗d5xa2 ♖d1-c1** and assumed her rook was lost, but **3 ♖d1-f1** everything holds together rather nicely.

Rudenko-Rootare
USSR 1956

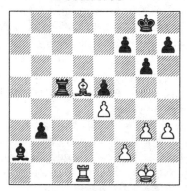

This is a classic example of the dangers of pessimistic thinking in chess. One starts to fear shadows that are not even there. And those who suffer from such pessimism tend to be the ones most ready to die.

Do we learn from our mistakes in chess? Maybe. Our beloved game contains so many possibilities, that there will always be plenty of mistakes left to be made – but the same mistake twice?! Our beloved heroine shows that once is never enough...

Stekalovsky-Rudenko
USSR 1961

When confronted by the rook move attacking her queen, Rudenko threw in the towel. After all, if she moves the queen there is a back rank mate. So why not resign?

1 ... ♗d5xa2

A remarkable resource. So how many of you male chauvinists would have spotted it?

2 ♖b1xb2 ♖e2xb2

This is the point: Black has time to be calm. Wherever the queen moves, 3...♖b2-b1 will even the score. The resulting position is drawn.

It is often stated that good players make their own luck. My own view is that fortune favours the fighters. But there are times when providence looks down on those who have done nothing to deserve it.

Dekhanov-Yusupov
USSR 1981

Here, Artur Yusupov, renowned fighter and future World Championship Candidate, played the awful 1...♕f6-a6. His opponent saw that the queens would be exchanged and

rightly assessed that he had no chance in the endgame. What was so horribly, horribly wrong with this logic?

After **1...♕f6-a6** White is winning, and rather quickly: **2 g3-g4+ f5xg4+ 3 ♘e5xg4+ ♕a6xb5 4 ♘g4-f6#.**

Very pretty, but the lack of flight squares around the black king should have given him a big hint.

The next position earned White the accolade 'Blunder of the Year'. I think you will admit that it takes some beating, but first I should set the scene. Black, to move, offered White a draw. White quite rightly asked him to make his move first. (Practical hint: always do this in tournament play. You still have the option to accept once they have moved.)

Sztern-Lundquist
Australia 1983

Black thought for some time and found the brilliant...

1 ... ♕b6xb2+

Now White gets mated by force after 2 ♔b1xb2 ♖a3-b3+ 3 ♔b2-a2 ♖f8-a8+. White was in such a shock after this misfortune that he forgot about his draw option. Instead he resigned.

The only contender to the above occurred in a game between a Welsh master and a revered English gentleman of chess. Our Welsh friend was a rook ahead, but saw that his worthy adversary could force a perpetual check. So he politely asked, 'Would you like a draw?' 'No thank you.' was the reply. Ten minutes later the Englishman resigned; he pointed out immediately that there was a flaw in the perpetual that left him a full rook down.

The Welshman then asked the inevitable. 'My God, I thought you had offered me a drink. You should speak up, my good man.'

6 Studies

'The slowness of genius is hard to bear, but the slowness of mediocrity is intolerable.'
Henry Buckle

Like chess problems, studies are a whole universe in themselves. One could spend a lifetime composing studies, and several lifetimes trying to solve them. Whereas problems tend to require a specific solution in a set number of moves (i.e. mate in three), studies stipulate a result only; i.e. White to play and win/draw.

In this respect studies are more like real-life chess. The solution can be many moves deep, so one cannot use a method of elimination as one could in, for instance, a mate in two. But unlike in real chess, all the pieces have been arranged for a specific purpose, usually to give the study aesthetic appeal. Such situations rarely occur in practical chess, although particularly poignant finishes are referred to as 'study-like'.

By nature, studies are concerned with the later stages of the chess game. They are sometimes referred to as 'Endgame Studies', although as a non-expert I find this description somewhat misleading. The point is that some studies are genuine endgame studies, in the sense that they could well have occurred at the end of an over-the-board game. To solve such studies is not only pleasurable but beneficial for one's endgame play. Other studies are so bizarre that to refer to them as endgame studies seems slightly fatuous. The chances of them occurring in a normal game are just too remote.

For this reason I have decided to separate this chapter into two parts:

a) Endgame Studies;
b) Aesthetic Studies.

Part 'a' is concerned with true endgame studies, in particular king and pawn endgames. Without understanding the themes involved in the first ten studies one could simply not play king and pawn endgames. Similarly, it is essential to be familiar with the elementary themes in the rook and pawn endgame studies. Few would dispute the usefulness of such studies in over-the-board play.

Part 'b' is quite different. These are not everyday positions, but have been dreamed up by some of the best chess minds over the last two centuries. Although some of the themes are common, they are intertwined in such weird and wonderful ways that they are far removed from everyday chess. I do not wish to join the debate over their usefulness as training for OTB chess. My best advice is to be baffled and enjoy!

Although the two sections inevitably overlap, I personally feel that it is a worthwhile distinction between the probable and the highly improbable.

Endgame Studies

'It is a capital mistake to theorise before you have all the evidence. It biases the judgement.'
Arthur Conan Doyle 1859-1930

The first ten positions illustrate some of the main themes in king and pawn endgames: the opposition, triangulation and pawn breaks. I was once fortunate enough to be in an endgame seminar with Garry Kasparov; 'The most difficult endgames', he informed us at the beginning, 'are pawn endgames. This is because one error, however slight, will often be the difference between a win and a loss.'

Pawn endgame studies should teach us one thing: that we must treat pawn endgames with respect. Players assume that because there are no other pieces on the board, then it's all straightforward. However, there are so many tactical nuances that many games are thrown away at this final stage.

The most common kind of endgames are rook and pawn endgames. Take particular note of the Lucena position. In the minor-piece endgames, the most important theme is probably domination. When so few

pieces remain, dominating your opponent's piece will often be decisive.

1   **Anon**
                    1792

This is probably the most basic endgame study. White to play and win. If you don't know the solution, then you should. No one can play king and pawn endings without knowing this one.

2

This is another position that every player should know, although I've never seen it occur in a real game.

3

This study also revolves around the opposition theme. White to play and win. If Black were to move, White would have the opposition, and the black king would have to retreat and allow 2 ♔c5-b6.

4   **Cozio**
           1766

This ancient puzzle should not stump too many readers. White, to move, appears in dire straits, but pawn endgames are not always what they seem.

5

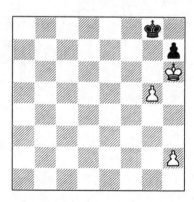

Another example of the importance of tempo in king and pawn endings.

6   **Schlage-Ahues**
           Berlin 1921

This occurred in a real game and illustrates an important property of the king. White to play and win.

7 **Réti**
1921

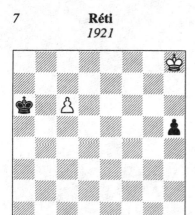

More of the same theme. This simple but beautiful study by Réti seems almost unbelievable. White to play and make a draw.

8 **Réti**
1928

Seven years later, Réti built on this theme. White is up against three pawns this time but it's still possible to draw.

9 **Dobias**
1926

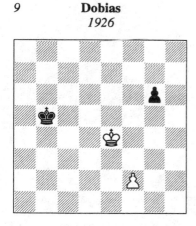

Chasing the black pawn immediately will not win for White, since Black has time to mop up the f-pawn. You have to finesse it.

10 **Neustadtl**
1890

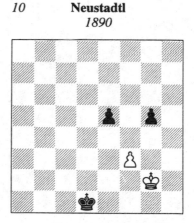

White is a pawn in arrears but there is a way to save the day.
CLUE: Remember the importance of opposition, but you need to be able to sustain it!

11   **Horwitz**
              1884

This is an easy one. Black will win back the pawn but White can create deadly threats.

12   **Lucena**
              1497

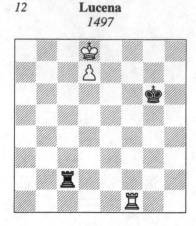

Every student of rook and pawn endings should know this position. How does White get the pawn home?

13   **Saavedra**
              1895

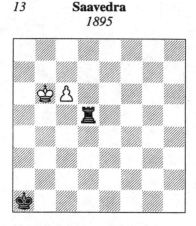

This is a well-known study by Saavedra. White to play and win; it looks obvious, but there is a twist.

14

Normally king and rook versus king and bishop is drawn, but here Black is caught in the dangerous corner (the one of the same colour as his bishop). White can dominate the bishop and win.

15

Black is threatening to continue 1...♘b7-d6+ 2 ♔e8-e7 ♘d6-c8+ with a draw. White must find a way to dominate the knight.

16 **Rauzer**
1928

White to play and win. Clearly the key is to keep the king well away from the corner.

17 **Prokeš**
1946

This is another teaser of considerable beauty. In normal chess one might resign without thinking. But there are always tricks in chess.
CLUE: Think Stalemate!

18 **Prokop**
1930

In this example it is the knight's turn to dominate the bishop; how can White win?
CLUE: You might expect the solution to start with a knight move; it doesn't!

19	**Duras**
	1902

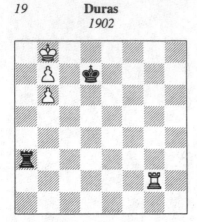

20	**S. Loyd**
	1860

White has two extra pawns, but can he win? The first move is clear but then it is hard to get the king out.
CLUE: A queen is worth more than a rook!

Finally, one from the great study master Sam Loyd. White to play and draw.
CLUE: See the Prokop study.

Aesthetic Studies

'It is when I struggle to be brief that I become obscure.'
Horace 65-8 BC

This is not a section for the faint-hearted.

One point must be emphasised before we begin: studies are difficult. In fact, they are very difficult. Remember that these are the choicest fruits of some very devious minds. Most of the studies in this section have won prizes for their complexity and artistic beauty. Do not get frustrated if you can't solve them after fifteen minutes. In fact, one should not expect to solve them at all. To be honest, I gave up on about half of

them and sneaked a look at the answers.

Most of these studies would never occur in a real game but we tend to try solving them as we would a normal position. Remember every piece is there for a reason. Do not make assumptions like you would in normal chess. If a pawn queens (whoops, there I go); sorry, if a pawn reaches the eighth rank, it does not have to become a queen. If your opponent attacks your queen, don't assume that you have to move it. A dangerous passed pawn might not be worth rounding up.

Several themes recur. If you are asked to find a draw, then be on the look out for possibilities of a stalemate, perpetual check or even a blockade. These can secure a half point however great the material imbalance. Even when searching for a win, be on the look-out for these themes as saving throes for Black.

When looking for a win, remember that the solution will usually demand something out of the ordinary. Often the most innocent-looking moves contain the key to the whole study. The black king should usually be the point of focus: any mating nets or dangerous checks?

The other point to bear in mind is that studies have many layered solutions. After finding what seems like an easy win, you may spot a brilliant resource for Black. Do not despair! You may find that you have an equally dramatic counter-blow to Black's saving throw.

1   **V. Evreinov**
            1959

White to play and win. There is something bizarre about this puzzle.
CLUE: The first move looks like the worst move on the board, but it isn't.

2   **A. & K. Sarychev**
            1928

Here White is to play and draw. It looks hopeless, since 1 c7-c8=♕ is met by 1...♗h7-f5+ and 2...♗f5xc8, when the b-pawn will queen.
CLUE: Recall the king's ability to zigzag without wasting time!

3   **U. Firdusi**

This study by Firdusi dates from around 1500 and is one of the oldest on record. White, to move, is a rook up, but Black threatens mate in one as well as the rook on c5. How does White secure the win?

4	**O. Duras** *1938*

This position causes one to do a double-take. Surely the board is the wrong way round? Aren't those queens *en prise*? Yes, the position is correct and White, to play, must find a draw.

5	**B. Horwitz** *1872*

Black has rather too many pawns for his own good. White to play and win.
CLUE: The key is to trap the king in a net and then effect a long manoeuvre to deliver the death-blow.

6	**G. Reichhelm** *1904*

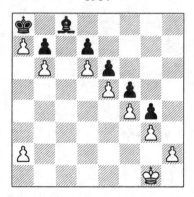

White to play and win. Normally you have to worry about your opponent's moves; here the worry is what can he move. The method for this is fairly obvious, but getting the move order right is very tricky!

7	**Troitsky** *1895*

This classic by Troitsky is one of my personal favourites. With so few pieces on the board it seems impossible that it can contain a solution of subtle beauty. White to play and win.

8   **S. Kozlowski**
     1938

White is to play and draw. It looks hopeless as there is no way to force the exchange of rook for pawn.
CLUE: The first move is obvious but the second involves moving the king to a most unlikely square!

9   **Gurgenidze**
     1980

Despite his extra pieces, White has problems. How does he win the game in dramatic fashion?
CLUE: The immediate sacrifice is obvious but look out for a twist.

10   **Evertz-Kieninger**
      Solingen 1964

This position actually occurred in a game; Black had just played ...♗b6xd4. This was a horrible blunder: why?

11   **Mitrofanov**
      1971

This is another situation where it seems inconceivable that White can win – but he can!
CLUE: You have to allow Black to queen in order to get his king.

| 12 | **M. Matous**
1984 | 13 | **Liburkin**
1931 |

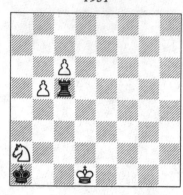

Here White is to play and win.
CLUE: Begin with a quiet move to
deny the king's last escape square;
then let him promote pawns!

Black seems to be defending, but
there is a way for White to win.
CLUE: You need to refer to Endgame Study 13 in order to see the
position that you are working towards.

| 14 | **A. J. Roycroft**
1972 | 15 | **J. Schlesinger**
1868 |

This is a study by one of Britain's
finest composers. Its appeal lies in
the way it combines tactical ideas
which could occur in over-the-
board play. White to play and win.
CLUE: Sacrifice on move one!

This is an old study by Schlesinger.
White is a rook ahead, but with so
many dangerous black pawns it
looks desperate; but White can
win.

16   **G. Nadareishvili**
        1987

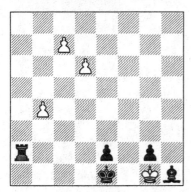

17   **A. Branton**
          1966

Here White is to play and win, and if you solve this one, you are a far better man than I.

CLUE: The first moves are obvious, but then you must think in terms of under-promotion.

This is another mission impossible, where White wins in dramatic fashion.

CLUE: Start off with a couple of bishop checks, then bring in the cavalry.

Solutions

Endgame Studies

(1)

1   ♔e1-d2

Many beginners will instinctively push their pawn with 1 e2-e4 but after several attempts they realise that the pawn cannot be pushed through from behind.

1   ...   ♚e8-d8
2   ♔d2-e3   ♚d8-e7
3   ♔e3-e4   ♚e7-e6

Black has gained what we term the 'opposition'; i.e. the two kings face each other and whoever is to move must stand down. However, White has a quiet move to regain the opposition.

4   e2-e3

The ability to lose a move is often critical in king and pawn endings. Now it is the black king who must stand down.

4   ...   ♚e6-d6
5   ♔e4-f5   ♚d6-e7
6   ♔f5-e5

Not 6 e3-e4 since after 6...♚e7-f7 Black has regained the opposition and the game will be drawn.

6   ...   ♚e7-d7
7   ♔e5-f6   ♚d7-d6
8   e3-e4   ♚d6-d7
9   e4-e5   ♚d7-e8
10 ♔f6-e6   ♚e8-f8
11 ♔e6-d7   ♚f8-f7

12 e5-e6+

And the pawn will promote.

(2)

1   b5-b6   c7xb6
2   a5-a6

This is the point: White overworks the b7-pawn.

2   ...   b7xa6
3   c5-c6

White wins

This position illustrates an important point. In pawn endings, the dynamism of pawn breaks can often count for more than numerical superiority.

(3)

1   ♔c5-d5   ♚c7-c8

Note that now if White plays 2 ♔d5-d6, then 2...♚c8-d8 3 c6-c7+ ♚d8-c8 draws, as 4 ♔d6-c6 is stalemate.

2   ♔d5-c4   ♚c8-d8

If 2...♚c8-c7, then 3 ♔c4-c5 and White has the opposition.

3   ♔c4-d4   ♚d8-c8
4   ♔d4-d5

White has performed a subtle triangular dance, the purpose of which was to lose a move. Remember the theme of triangulation in king and pawn endgames.

4   ...   ♚c8-c7
5   ♔d5-c5

Now White has regained the opposition.

5 ...	♔c7-d8
6 ♔c5-d6	♔d8-c8
7 c6-c7	♔c8-b7
8 ♔d6-d7	

White will queen his pawn.

(4)

1 c4-c5

The breakthrough is another essential theme.

1 ... b6xc5

White also wins after 1...b6-b5 2
a4xb5.

2 a4-a5	c5-c4
3 a5-a6	c4-c3
4 ♔f1-e1	

White can invest time to ensure
that it isn't just a pawn race.

4 ...	♔f3-e3
5 ♔e1-d1	

White wins.

(5)

1 h2-h3

The impetuous 1 h2-h4 only
draws; e.g. 1...♔g8-h8 2 h4-h5 ♔h8-
g8 3 g5-g6 h7xg6 4 h5xg6 ♔g8-h8 5
g6-g7+ ♔h8-g8 and draws.

1 ...	♔g8-h8
2 h3-h4	♔h8-g8
3 h4-h5	♔g8-h8
4 g5-g6	h7xg6
5 h5xg6	♔h8-g8
6 g6-g7	♔g8-f7
7 ♔h6-h7	

White wins.

(6)

1 ♔f7-e6

1 ♔f7-e7 ♔b2-c3 2 ♔e7-d7 ♔c3-
c4 3 ♔d7-c7 ♔c4-c5 4 ♔c7-b7 ♔c5-
d6 5 ♔b7xa7 ♔d6-c7 and now we
have reached a well-known draw.

1 ...	♔b2-c3
2 ♔e6-d5	

This interferes with the king's
progress towards the critical c7-
square.

2 ...	♔c3-b4
3 ♔d5-c6	♔b4-a5
4 ♔c6-b7	♔a5-b5
5 ♔b7xa7	♔b5-c6
6 ♔a7-b8	

White wins. One strange property
of a chessboard is that one can travel
in a zigzag route as quickly as moving in a straight line. This becomes
very relevant in king and pawn endings.

(7)

1 ♔h8-g7	h5-h4
2 ♔g7-f6	

The trick is to use the zigzag. Now
2...h4-h3 3 ♔f6-e7 h3-h2 4 c6-c7
♔a6-b7 5 ♔e7-d7 leads to a draw. So
Black must stop the pawn.

| 2 | ... | ♔a6-b6 |
| 3 | ♔f6-e5 | |

The zigzag continues. If Black plays 3...♔b6xc6, 4 ♔e5-f4 catches the pawn.

| 3 | ... | h4-h3 |

Now White can support his pawn.

4	♔e5-d6	h3-h2
5	c6-c7	h2-h1=♕
6	c7-c8=♕	

With a draw.

(8)

| 1 | ♔h5-g6 | ♔a6-b6 |
| 2 | ♔g6xg7 | f6-f5 |

2...h6-h5 3 ♔g7xf6 h5-h4 4 ♔f6-e5 gives us the position we have just discussed.

3	♔g7-f6	f5-f4
4	♔f6-e5	f4-f3
5	♔e5-d6	f3-f2
6	c6-c7	f2-f1=♕
7	c7-c8=♕	

A theoretically drawn position is reached.

(9)

| 1 | ♔e4-d4 | |

This is a very calm solution, preventing the king from coming for the f-pawn.

| 1 | ... | ♔b5-b4 |

1...♔b5-c6 2 ♔d4-e5 ♔c6-c5 3 f2-f4 wins.

| 2 | f2-f4 | |

White needs the f-pawn up the board so it can be secured after he has gobbled the g-pawn.

2	...	♔b4-b3
3	♔d4-e5	♔b3-c4
4	♔e5-f6	♔c4-d5
5	♔f6xg6	♔d5-e4
6	f4-f5	

White wins.

(10)

| 1 | ♔g2-h1 | |

The only way to keep the opposition. After 1 ♔g2-f1 ♔d1-d2 2 ♔f1-f2 ♔d2-d3 the white king can no longer oppose.

1	...	♔d1-d2
2	♔h1-h2	♔d2-e3
3	♔h2-g3	♔e3-d4
4	♔g3-g4	♔d4-e3
5	♔g4-g3	

There is no way to win.

(11)

| 1 | ♔f4-f5 | ♔h6-h7 |

1...♖g8xg7 2 ♖g1-h1#.

2	♔f5-f6	♖g8-e8
3	♖g1-h1+	♔h7-g8
4	♖h1-h8#	

(12)

| 1 | ♖f1-f4 | |

White must build a bridge, so that his king can exit via the e-file.

1	...	🜚c2-c1
2	♔d8-e7	🜚c1-e1+
3	♔e7-d6	🜚e1-d1+
4	♔d6-e6	🜚d1-e1+
5	♔e6-d5	🜚e1-d1+
6	🜚f4-d4	

White wins.

(13)

| 1 | c6-c7 | 🜚d5-d6+ |
| 2 | ♔b6-b5 | |

White cannot go to the c-file in view of 2...🜚d6-d1.

2	...	🜚d6-d5+
3	♔b5-b4	🜚d5-d4+
4	♔b4-b3	🜚d4-d3+
5	♔b3-c2	

The checks have run out, but there is a trick.

| 5 | ... | 🜚d3-d4 |

Now after 6 c7-c8=♕ 🜚d4-c4+ 7 ♕c8xc4 it is stalemate!

However, White has another method:

| 6 | c7-c8=🜚!! | |

Black must defend against 7 🜚c8-a8+.

| 6 | ... | 🜚d4-a4 |

| 7 | ♔c2-b3 | |

Black cannot defend both the rook and the mate on c1, and so White wins.

(14)

| 1 | 🜚f7-f1 | ♗g1-h2 |
| 2 | 🜚f1-f2 | ♗h2-g3 |

2...♗h2-g1 3 🜚f2-g2 and wherever the bishop moves, the rook will attack it.

| 3 | 🜚f2-g2 | |

The bishop would like to go to f4 but this fails to 4 ♔g6-f5+. Similarly, 3...♗g3-h4 loses after the reply 4 ♔g6-h5+.

3	...	♗g3-d6
4	🜚g2-d2	♗d6-e7
5	🜚d2-c2	

Black is powerless against 6 🜚c2-c8(+).

(15)

1	♔e8-e7	♘b7-d8
2	♗d3-e4	♘d8-f7
3	♗e4-d5	♘f7-d8
4	♔e7-e8	

Black is in zugzwang.

(16)

1	♗b4-c5	♚a6-a5
2	♔c6-b7	♚a5-b5
3	♗c5-b6	♚b5-c4
4	♔b7-c6	♚c4-b3
5	♗b6-c5	♚b3-c4
6	♗c5-d6	♚c4-d4
7	♔c6-b5	♚d4-d5
8	♗d6-h2	

It is essential to keep the bishop on this diagonal in order to prevent the black king from reaching the drawing corner. On h2 the bishop is also away from a possible gain of tempo by attack from the black king.

8	...	♚d5-e6
9	♔b5xa4	♚e6-d7
10	♔a4-b5	♚d7-c8
11	♔b5-c6	

And wins.

(17)

1	♘a5-b3+	

Black must capture since otherwise 2 ♘b3-d2 would cover the queening square.

1	...	♗c4xb3+
2	♔a4-a3	

If the pawn promotes to a queen or a rook White is stalemated, and there are no useful underpromotions. Draw!

(18)

1	♔e6-e5	♗e4-a8
2	♘a4-b6	♗a8-b7

Black seems to be holding comfortably since 3 ♔e5-d6 fails to 3...♚e8-d8. But let's not forget our old friend the opposition.

3	♔e5-e6	♗b7-c6

After 3...♚e8-d8 4 ♔e6-d6 ♗b7-h1, 5 ♘b6-d5 shuts the bishop out.

4	♔e6-d6	♗c6-b7
5	♔d6-c7	♗b7-h1
6	♘b6-c8	♗h1-a8
7	♔c7-b8	♚e8-d8
8	♘c8-d6	

When the bishop moves it is shut out by 9 ♘d6-b7.

8	...	♚d8-d7
9	♘d6-b7	

Not 9 ♔b8xa8, when 9...♚d7-c7 leads to a theoretical draw.

9	...	♚d7-c6
10	♔b8xa8	♚c6-c7
11	♘b7-d6	

When the black king moves, the white king comes to b8, and White wins.

(19)

1	♖g2-d2+	♚d7-e7

Now 2 ♔b8-c8 is kicked straight back by 2...♖a3-c3+.

2	♖d2-d6	

A powerful move, because after 2...♚e7xd6 3 ♔b8-c8 there is nothing to stop the b-pawn.

| 2 | ... | ♖a3-c3 |
| 3 | ♖d6-c6 | |

Still Black cannot capture, this time because 4 ♔b8-a7 assures promotion.

3	...	♖c3-d3
4	♖c6-c1	♔e7-d8
5	♖c1-a1	

Having secured the a-file the king can now step aside to let the pawn promote. White wins.

(20)

| 1 | ♗a4-d7 | h3-h2 |
| 2 | ♗d7-c6+ | ♔g2-g1 |

2...♘h4-f3 3 ♔e1-e2 is drawn.

| 3 | ♗c6-h1 | ♔g1xh1 |
| 4 | ♔e1-f2 | |

This is a theoretical draw, since the knight cannot displace the king from the squares f1/f2. Note that 4 ♔e1-f1 would lose after 4...♘h4-f3 5 ♔f1-f2 ♘f3-d2 and White must let the black king out.

Aesthetic Studies

(1)

| 1 | ♖d4-e4 | |

This is the only move that wins. Any other rook move allows 1...d5-d4 with discovered check to the white king. It is worth a rook to keep the critical a1-h8 diagonal open.

1	...	d5xe4+
2	♔f3-g2	e4-e3+
3	♔g2-g1	

Now the king is safe from any checks, and Black must prevent the advance of the f-pawn.

| 3 | ... | ♗g8-f7 |

4	e6xf7	♕c6xc5
5	f7-f8=♕+	♕c5xf8
6	f6-f7+	♕f8-g7+

It would seem that Black's problems are now solved, since after 7 ♗a1xg7+ ♔h8xg7 White is losing. However ...

| 7 | ♔g1-h2 | ♕g7xa1 |
| 8 | f7-f8=♕# | |

A very economical finish.

(2)

1	♔d7-c8	b7-b5
2	♔c8-d7	b5-b4
3	♔d7-d6	

3 ♔d7-e6 loses to 3...♔e4.

| 3 | ... | ♗h7-f5 |
| 4 | ♔d6-e5 | |

This is the point. 4...b4-b3 5 ♔e5xf5 is a simple draw. But if the bishop moves, then 5 ♔e5-d4 permits White time to capture the pawn. Black cannot win.

(3)

| 1 | ♖c5-h5 | |

A simple but beautiful solution. Black has no option but to take the rook since 2 ♖a8-a6# is threatened.

1	...	♖h1xh5
2	♖a8-a6+	♔d6-c5
3	♖a6-a5+	

White regains the rook, and so he wins.

(4)

| 1 | ♕e2-d3 | |

Now if Black grabs the queen he delivers stalemate, but 1...b2-b1=♕ 2 ♕d3-c3+ is also drawn. Nevertheless Black still has some tricks.

1 ...	♕f1-d1+
2 ♕d3xd1+	b2-b1=♕

If 3 ♕d1xb1+, then 3...♔a1xb1 again wins for Black.

3 ♔a4xa3	♕b1xd1

Stalemate!

(5)

1 c2-c3+	♔d4-c5
2 ♘b2-a4+	♔c5-b5
3 c3-c4+	♔b5-a6
4 ♗h1-c6	

Black's king is trapped and White is ready to begin the king march. The white king heads up the board by way of c2-d1-e2-f1-g2-h3-g4-f5-e6-d7-c8. Then ♗c6-b7#.

(6)

1 h2-h3	g4xh3
2 ♔g1-h1	h3-h2
3 g3-g4	f5xg4
4 ♔h1xh2	g4-g3+
5 ♔h2-g1	g3-g2
6 f4-f5	

Starting to see a pattern?

6 ...	e6xf5
7 ♔g1xg2	f5-f4
8 a2-a4	f4-f3+
9 ♔g2-f1	f3-f2
10 e5-e6	d7xe6
11 ♔f1xf2	♗c8-d7

This position had to be reached eventually, but note that White has won enough time to advance the a-pawn.

12 a4-a5	♗d7-c6
13 ♔f2-e3	♗c6-d7

13...e6-e5 is no use since after 14 ♔e3-d3 the bishop cannot stay on the long diagonal.

14 ♔e3-d4	♗d7-c8
15 ♔d4-e5	♗c8-d7
16 ♔e5-f6	♗d7-c8
17 ♔f6-e7	e6-e5
18 d6-d7	♗c8xd7
19 ♔e7xd7	e5-e4
20 ♔d7-c7	e4-e3
21 a5-a6	

And White wins with a move to spare.

(7)

1 ♗e3-h6+	♔f8-g8
2 g6-g7	♔g8-f7

2...e7-e5 would lose to 3 ♔d5-e6 e5-e4 4 ♔e6-f6 e4-e3 5 ♗h6xe3 h7-h5 6 ♗e3-g5.

3 g7-g8=♕+	♔f7xg8
4 ♔d5-e6	

Without either the h-pawn or the e-pawn it would be a trivial draw. Here, however, Black is obliged to bury himself in his own tomb.

4 ...	♔g8-h8
5 ♔e6-f7	e7-e5

Black is not stalemated.

6 ♗h6-g7#	

(8)

1 ♖a7-a1	♔g3-g2
2 ♔g8-h8	

Allowing the pawn to queen with check!

2 ...	♗d3-f1
3 ♖a1-a7	

The point.

3 ...	h2-h1=♕+

3...♔g2-g3 4 ♖a7-g7+ draws.

4 ♖a7-h7	♕h1-g1
5 ♖h7-g7+	

With a draw.

(9)

> 1 ♕g1-f1+   ♚e2xf1
> 2 ♗e8-b5+

If Black captures the knight with
2...♚f1xe1, 3 ♘a3-c2+ picks up the
queen and wins the game, since the
f-pawns can easily be rounded up.
But Black has a defensive try.

> 2 ...   ♛d4-c4
> 3 ♘a3xc4

This is the key move, since 3
♗b5xc4+ ♚f1xe1 4 ♘a3-c2+ ♚e1-
d2 5 ♘c2-d4 ♚d2-c3 is a draw.

> 3 ...   f2xe1=♛

Black has his queen back but it
only help White's mating net.

> 4 ♘c4-e3++   ♚f1-f2
> 5 ♘e3-g4#

(10)

> 1 ♗g3-f4

Remarkably, Black now has no
way to stop the h-pawn.

> 1 ...   ♚e4xf4
> 2 h5-h6

and Black soon resigned.

(11)

> 1 ♚e8-f8   f4-f3
> 2 f5-f6   e7xf6
> 3 g5-g6

Now it is all fixed; both sides push
their pawns.

> 3 ...   f3-f2
> 4 h4-h5   f2-f1=♛

It looks as if Black has won the
race, but the queen has promoted on
a useless square.

> 5 h5-h6

Black cannot prevent the mate.

> 5 ...   g7xh6

> 6 g6-g7+   ♚h8-h7
> 7 g7-g8=♛#

(12)

> 1 h2-h3   b2xc1=♛
> 2 ♗f8-e7+   ♛c1-g5
> 3 ♚h1-h2

Another calm move to threaten
mate with 4 g2-g3.

> 3 ...   c2-c1=♛
> 4 ♘e4-d2

This creates a dual mating threat:
5 ♘d2-f3 and 5 g2-g3.

> 4 ...   ♛a2xd2

If 4...♛c1xd2, then 5 ♖e1-e4+
♛d2-f4 6 ♖e4xf4#.

> 5 ♖e1-e4+   ♛d2-f4+

Black has three queens and one is
giving check, but they are helpless to
prevent mate.

> 6 g2-g3#

(13)

> 1 ♘a2-c1   ♖c5xb5
> 2 c6-c7   ♖b5-d5+

It looks like Black is holding the
draw since after 3 ♚e2 ♖e5+ the
rook intercepts the c-pawn.

> 3 ♘c1-d3   ♖d5xd3+
> 4 ♚d1-c2   ♖d3-d4
> 5 c7-c8=♖

And we are back to that old finesse; see the earlier position by
Saavedra.

(14)

> 1 ♖d6-d5+   ♛a8xd5
> 2 ♖f2-f5+   ♚e5-d6
> 3 ♖f5xd5+   ♚d6xd5

So far this is fairly easy to see.
The real skill is in seeing that this

position is not just a simple draw. After all, it is the wrong coloured rook's pawn.

    4 h4-h5   ♔d5-e5
    5 h5-h6   ♔e5-f6

Now 6 h6-h7 ♔f6-g7 is just a simple draw; but White has a finesse.

    6 ♗h3-f5

I've actually seen this trick occur in a real game. Black's next move must allow the h-pawn to queen.

(15)
    1 ♔d3-e2   ♔g2xh1

Black has no other constructive moves.

    2 ♔e2-f1

Black is now in a hopeless state; he can give away his queenside pawns, but ultimately he will have to move the bishop. For example:

    2 ...   c5-c4
    3 ♗d5xc4   a3-a2
    4 ♗c4xa2   b4-b3
    5 ♗a2xb3   ♗e5-d4
    6 e4-e5   d6xe5
    7 ♗a2-d5+

Mate follows next move.

(16)
    1 d6-d7   ♖a2-d2

Or 1...♔e1-d1 2 d7-d8=♕+ ♖a2-d2 3 ♕d8-h4 e2-e1=♕+ 4 ♕h4xe1+ ♔d1xe1 5 c7-c8=♕ ♖d1 6 ♕c2 winning for White.

    2 d7-d8=♕   ♖d2xd8

So far, so obvious, but now if 3 c7xd8=♕ (or =♖) then it's stalemate.

    3 c7xd8=♗   ♔e1-d2
    4 ♗d8-h4   ♔d2-c3
    5 b4-b5   ♔c3-c4

It all looks like plain sailing for White but there are still tricks left in the position.

    6 b5-b6   ♔c4-b5
    7 b6-b7   ♔b5-a6
    8 b7-b8=♖

Avoiding the final trick. 8 b7-b8=♕ would only draw after 8...e2-e1=♕ 9 ♗h4xe1 stalemate.

(17)
    1 ♗b6-d8+   ♔h4-g3
    2 ♗d8-c7+   ♔g3-f3

This is the only way to make a fight of it. After 2...♔g3-f2 3 ♘c5-e4+ ♔f2-g1 4 ♘b3-d2 the king will be mated.

    3 ♘b3-d4+   ♔f3-f2
    4 ♘c5-e4+   ♔f2-f1
    5 ♘e4-d2+   ♔f1-f2
    6 ♗c7-g3+

This is the coup; Black must walk into the net.

    6 ...   ♔f2xg3
    7 ♘d2-e4+   ♔g3-h4
    8 ♘d4-f3+   ♔h4-h5
    9 ♘e4-g3#

The way the black army prevents its own monarch from reaching safety is almost the stuff of tragic poetry.

7 Direct Mate Problems

In the previous chapter we saw many endgame positions in which White's target was to force a win or draw. However, by far the most common type of puzzle involves White delivering mate in a fixed number of moves. While these are not so relevant to the over-the-board game as win or draw positions, they are very popular with all classes of players. Their advantage is that the conclusion is completely clear-cut – there can't be any argument about whether a position is mate or not, whereas win or draw positions are often tricky to evaluate unless you are well up on endgame theory.

In this chapter you will find 20 positions in which White has to force mate in a given number of moves. In many cases it is clear that the position is winning for White, but in every case there is just one way to finish Black off within the specified time limit. The ingenuity of composers knows no bounds; you will discover (assuming that you don't peek at the solutions!) some of the most extraordinary manoeuvres which the chessmen can perform.

Some compositions are really tough, but I have gone for the relatively easy end of the spectrum (but note the word relatively – many of these are not straightforward). If you work your way through from the first position, you will find that some ideas recur, so although the problems get longer as the chapter proceeds, you shouldn't find the later ones harder than the earlier examples.

In every position White is to play and the aim is to mate Black, against any defence, in the number of moves given under the diagram.

The technical word *zugzwang* is used in the solutions. This refers to the situation in which a player is obliged to weaken his own position by the act of making a move, i.e. he would like to sit tight and do nothing, but the laws of chess oblige him to move something, and every choice is bad. Many puzzles make use of *zugzwang*, so you should not always be looking for a threatening move; it may be better to put Black in a situation where he has to destroy his own position.

This chapter is divided into two parts. The first section contains only fairly elementary mates in two and three. After tackling these, you should be ready for a set of slightly more tricky positions, including not only mates in two and three, but also some longer problems.

1   **W. Suesman**

2   **E. Winter-Wood**
1886

White to play and mate in two. Queen and knight are a powerful combination. Note that if it were Black to play first, White would mate on the next move, suggesting that the solution involves waiting.

White to play and mate in two. If it were Black to play, all moves except 1...b4-b3 would allow mate in one. If White can deal with this possibility without losing his current threats, he is home and dry.

3   **N. Macleod**
1951

4   **Z. Drobot**
1986

White to play and mate in two. The white rook, knight and bishop are already restraining the black king, so White must deliver a queen mate without allowing the black rook to delay the end.

White to play and mate in two. Problems always have unique solutions, so although the position is symmetrical, the proximity of one side of the board must help to create a unique key move.

5   **Dr F. Palitzsch**
            1917

White to play and mate in two. This problem is tricky in spite of the material advantage. Each piece must have a role in at least one of the variations, so the kings must come closer together, but how?

6   **L. Owen**
            1922

White to play and mate in two. White has to create a threat since Black has many waiting moves. The pawns on f3 and b2 suggest that 1...♚c5-d4 will be a move that you must answer.

7   **K. Howard**

White to play and mate in two. Why is the black pawn on d7? The only reason is that it must block an escape route, probably when the king is on e6. Don't forget to lift the stalemate!

8   **Dr R. Leopold**
            1917

White to play and mate in two. The central pawn mass helps to wall in the black king. It is unlikely the composer could resist the visual impact of three pawns on the e-file, so the rook on e3 ought to stay put.

9   **W. Shinkman**
              1877

White to play and mate in two. The black king is already very restricted, but the killer blow is less than obvious. The problem is what to do about 1...d7-d6.

10   **C. Mansfield**
               1962

White to play and mate in two. The pawn on the seventh rank suggests that the solution will involve promotion. As this is a problem you should remember that promoting to a queen is not the only option.

11   **E. Holladay**

White to play and mate in two. Another pawn on the seventh rank; another under-promotion? Some subtlety is required as the rook on h5 is feeling threatened.

12   **C. Mansfield**
               1914

White to play and mate in two. This is a slightly tricky problem as there are several variations. A direct threat is essential since Black has a bishop and rook that are free.

13   **E. Cook**
1911

White to play and mate in three. This problem is based on the standard technique of winning with king and rook against king.

14   **R. Brieger**
1985

White to play and mate in three. This simple one proves length does not equte to difficulty. White must play forcefully because Black is threatening some spite checks.

15   **P. Torngren**
1928

White to play and mate in three. The apparent symmetry of the position suggests that there might be two solutions. If you can see why not, then you are well on the way to solving the problem.

16   **A. de Musset**
1792

White to play and mate in three. The interaction of the three knights is interesting, especially since a king and two knights cannot normally force mate against even a lone king.

17   **K. Howard**
          1925

White to play and mate in three. Black's main defence is 1...h7-h5, creating some space for his king. You might start by analysing why taking the knight doesn't work.

18   **W. Shinkman**
          1872

White to play and mate in three. The two rooks limit Black's options, but White must be wary of giving stalemate. The position is nearly symmetrical, but of course there is only one solution.

19   **S. Loyd**
          1856

White to play and mate in three. First try to find a mating method if Black keeps to the edge of the board, since this should be easier to visualise than more open play.

20   **W. Shinkman**
          1890

White to play and mate in three. Black's king must be given a square since he currently has no moves, and you should be warned that the first move is quite sly.

Solutions

1)
1 ♕d2-d1, with mate on a4 or g4 according to Black's king move. The play is entirely symmetrical.

2)
1 ♖e3-b3 with the following possibilities: 1...e4-e3 2 ♕e1xe3#; 1...f5-f4 2 ♕c1-a1#; 1...♔e5-d4 2 ♕e1-c3#; 1...♔e5-f4 2 ♕e1-g3#; 1...♔e5-e6 2 ♕e1xe4#.

3)
1 ♔h6-g6 setting up 2 ♕h7-h1# in response to a rook move onto the a- to e-files. If the black rook moves to f6, f7, g5 or h5 then the king can capture to deliver mate. Any other rook move allows 2 ♕h7-b7#, as does a pawn move.

4)
1 ♘c2-e3 setting up mates from d5 or d1. Against the try 1 ♘c2-a3 Black had the defence 1...♕c8-f5, but the equivalent move fails because there is no file to the left of the a-file.

5)
1 ♖e8-e1, when taking the rook allows 2 ♗a1-c3#. 1...♔d2-c2 runs into 1 ♕h5-d1#, while the final choice of 1...♔d2-d3 allows 2 ♕h5-e2#.

6)
1 ♕h4-d8 sneaking around the back with 2 ♕d8-b6.

7)
1 ♔c3-c4 with three variations: 1...♔e5-e6 2 ♔c4-d4#; 1...♔e5-e4 2 ♕b3-e3#; 1...♔e5-f4 2 ♔c4-d5#.

8)
1 ♕b3-g8 with a variety of mates delivered on the f- and g- files depending on the defence.

9)
1 ♗b3-a4 works, since taking the knight permits the bishop to mate by returning to its original position. 1...d7-d6 is answered by 2 ♘b5-c7#. 1...f7-f5 2 ♕h7-g8# is not any better, nor is 1...f7-f6 2 ♘d5-c7#.

10)
1 ♕f8-e8 with the variations: 1...♘g8-e7 2 f7-f8=♕#; 1...h6-h5 2 f7xg8=♘#; 1...♘g8xf6 2 f7-f8=♘#.

11)
1 ♕d7-d5 when the critical line is 1...♖g7-g5 2 f7-f8=♘#.

12)
1 ♘c5-d7 (threatening 2 ♘a4-b2#) with the variations: 1...♖d3-d4 2 ♘d7-e5#; 1...♖d3-d2 2 ♕h8-c3#;

1...d5-d4 2 ♕h8-g8#; 1...♗e1-c3 2 ♗a2xb3#.

13)

1 ♖f5-f6, and now if Black takes a rook, White recaptures and mates the following move. After 1...♗g7-f8 or 1...♗g7-h8, White checks on h8 and then mates on f8.

14)

1 g2-g4+ h4xg3 2 e3-e4+ ♔f5-f4 3 ♖a6-f6#

15)

1 ♖b6-d6 ♔c5-b5 2 ♔a7-b7 ♔b5-any 3 ♖d6-d5#. The symmetrical line fails because the king flees to b8.

16)

1 ♖h7-d7 forces Black to capture to prevent 2 ♘g4-f6. Then 2 ♘e5-c6 and 3 ♘g4-f6# follows.

17)

1 ♖f1-f6 aiming to manoeuvre to g8 via g6 if given the chance. Moreover, 1...h7-h5 allows 2 ♖h2xh5+ g6xh5 3 ♖f6-h6#.

18)

1 f6xe7 with the following lines: 1...♔e6-f6 2 e7-e8=♗ ♔f6-e6 3 ♖h7-h6#; 1...♔e6-d7 2 e7-e8=♕+ ♔d7xe8 (or 2...♔d7xd6 3 ♕e8-g6#) 3 ♖a5-a8#; 1...♔e6xd6 2 e7-e8=♖ ♔d6-c6 3 ♖e8-e6#.

19)

1 ♗f1-c4 when the only difficult line is 1...♔g4-f5 2 ♕e3-g3 with either 2...♔f5-e4 3 ♗c4-d3# or 2...♔f5-f6 3 ♕g3-g5#.

20)

1 ♕b5-b2 ♔c8-d7 2 ♕b2-e5 ♔d7-c6 (2...♔d7-c8 3 ♕e5-c7#) 3 ♕e5-d5#.

1   **N. Easter**
1929

White to play and mate in two. Black can only move his king and bishop, but that doesn't mean that it is easy to finish him off.

CLUE: Don't be afraid of allowing Black to give check.

2   **C. Mansfield**
1927

White to play and mate in two. This position is by one of Britain's greatest composers, who died in 1984.

CLUE: The king should be used actively.

3   **A. Stubbs**
1923

White to play and mate in two. White has a massive force massed around Black's king, but subtlety is needed to mate in two.

CLUE: The queen has to lie in ambush.

4   **R. Batchelor**
1924

White to play and mate in two. Sometimes the first move of a problem is so spectacular that the problem is easy to solve.

CLUE: White must sacrifice to as many enemy men as possible.

5   **J. Warton**
              1918

White to play and mate in two. In the diagram, every Black move allows an immediate mate. Can White preserve the *status quo*?

6   **E. Letzen**
              1921

White to play and mate in two. It is possible to simply take the queen, but this doesn't lead to mate in two. CLUE: In the diagram Black is threatening 1...♛g5xb5. How can White nullify this threat?

7   **R. Thomson**
              1921

White to play and mate in two. The solution uses the full area of the chessboard.
CLUE: Geometrical ideas abound in problems.

8   **A. C. White**
              1920

White to play and mate in two. Black's king is trapped, but it is not so easy to force mate in two. CLUE: The solution involves one of the most spectacular moves in the book.

9   **A. Sparke**
1918

White to play and mate in two. Black's bishop and knight are lined up against White's king, and the possibility of pinning the queen or checking stops several ideas from working. What is the way through?

10   **W. Speckmann**
1968

White to play and mate in three. This is an easy start to the mates in three...true or false?
CLUE: The first move is with the bishop, but only one square works.

11   **W. Speckmann**
1964

White to play and mate in three. Black has only his king, but this means that you must be careful not to deliver stalemate.
CLUE: It isn't forced to promote to a queen.

12   **V. Cisar**
1909

White to play and mate in three. This is quite a tricky position as White must trap Black's king, but without giving stalemate.
CLUE: White has to hide his queen in an ambush.

13   W. von Holzhausen
1903

White to play and mate in three. A simple idea...once you have seen it.
CLUE: Geometry rears its ugly head.

14   A. Kauders
1903

White to play and mate in three. The first move is absolutely stunning.
CLUE: Who needs a queen to mate?

15   L. Kubbel
1909

White to play and mate in three. A queen and two bishops are a formidable attacking force, but this is not as easy as it looks.
CLUE: White must avoid stalemate, so one piece must hide away.

16   H. Meyer
1903

White to play and mate in three. There is only one idea in this position, but even so it may take you a few minutes to spot it.
CLUE: White must avoid giving stalemate after his *second* move.

17   **A. Werle**
        1945

White to play and mate in four. This is a classic puzzle and if you haven't seen it before, then you should be prepared for a surprise. CLUE: Black doesn't have to promote to a queen.

18   **E. Guttmann**
        1935

White to play and mate in four. White would like to mate along the third rank, but this requires care. CLUE: Once you have promoted to a particular piece, you can't change your mind.

19   **V. Savchenko**
        1950

White to play and mate in six. Black's king has no moves, but White's bishop is the wrong colour for an easy mate. CLUE: White must sacrifice his bishop.

20   **F. Davidenko**
        1979

White to play and mate in seven. This position combines various ideas from earlier puzzles. CLUE: The first part is based on a similar idea to puzzle 16, while the second part resembles puzzle 19.

Solutions

(1)

    1 ♔f1-g2

Zugzwang.

a) 1 ...   ♗b2xd4+
    2 ♗e1-f2#

b) 1 ...   ♗b2-c1+
    2 ♗b3-c2#

c) 1 ...   ♗b2-c3+
    2 ♗e1-d2#

(2)

The only way that White can force mate in two is to expose his king to checks from the enemy queen.

    1 ♔f4-e5

Threat 2 ♖d8-c8#

a) 1 ...   ♕b1xe4+
    2 ♗h1xe4#

b) 1 ...   ♕b1-b2+
    2 ♘e4-c3#

c) 1 ...   ♕b1-b5+
    2 ♘e4-c5#

d) 1 ...   ♕b1-b8+
    2 ♘e4-d6#

e) 1 ...   ♕b1-b7
    2 ♕a7-c5#

f) 1 ...   ♕b1-b6
    2 ♕a7-d7#

g) 1 ...   ♘f5-d6
    2 ♖d8xd6#

(3)

    1 ♕h5-h1

Zugzwang. White's queen is now lurking behind the enemy rook and knight. When one of them moves, the queen leaps out along the newly opened line to deliver mate. The fact that Black's king now has a potential escape route via g6 doesn't help.

a) 1 ...   ♖f3xf2
    2 ♕h1-e4#

b) 1 ...   ♘g1-h3
    2 ♕h1-b1#

c) 1 ...   ♖f3-f4+
    2 ♕h1-e4#

d) 1 ...   g5-g4
    2 ♕h1-h5#

e) 1 ...   ♔f5xg6
    2 ♕h1-h7#

(4)

    1 ♗e4-d3

Threats 2 ♕e6-e4# and 2 ♕e6-e3#. Surprisingly, these mates don't appear after the captures of the white bishop. Instead, White's king administers the *coup de grâce*.

a) 1 ...   ♖c3xd3
    2 ♕e6-g4#

b) 1 ...   ♖c8-e8
    2 ♔d6xc6#

c) 1 ...   ♖c8-d8
    2 ♕e6-e4#

d) 1 ...   ♖c3xc5
    2 ♕e6-e4#

e) 1 ...   ♔d4xd3
    2 ♔d6-e7#

f) 1 ...   ♗c2xd3
    2 ♗d2-e3#

(5)

   1 ♔g2-h2

Zugzwang.

a) 1 ...   ♖a2xa8
     2 ♖h8xa8#

b) 1 ...   ♖a2-a3
     2 ♕a8xa3#

c) 1 ...   c3-c2
     2 ♗f2-d4#

d) 1 ...   ♖b1-c1
     2 ♖h1xc1#

e) 1 ...   ♖b1xh1+
     2 ♕a8xh1#

(6)

The key is to block the line b5-e2, thereby preventing Black's queen interposing on e2 after she takes the b5-rook.

   1 ♖e4-c4

Zugzwang.

a) 1 ...   ♗e1-d2
     2 ♔f3-f2#

b) 1 ...   ♗e1-g3
     2 ♔f3-g2#

c) 1 ...   ♗e1-f2
     2 ♔f3xf2#

d) 1 ...   ♗e1xh4
     2 ♔f3-e4#

e) 1 ...   ♕g5xb5
     2 ♔f3-e3#

f) 1 ...   ♕g5-e5
     2 ♔f3-g2#

(7)

   1 ♕h1-a8

Threat 2 ♖f4-f3#.

a) 1 ...   ♕f7xf5
     2 ♖f4-e4#

b) 1 ...   d6-d5
     2 ♕a8-b8#

c) 1 ...   ♖e2xf2+
     2 ♖f4xf2#

d) 1 ...   ♖e2xc2
     2 ♕a8-e4#

e) 1 ...   ♕f7-d5
     2 ♕a8-h8#

f) 1 ...   ♗c4-d5
     2 ♕a8-a1#

(8)

   1 ♕f6-a1

Zugzwang. This is an amazing move, not only hiding the queen away in the corner, but also allowing Black to take it with check.

a) 1 ...   ♕b1xa1+
     2 c2-c3#

b) 1 ...   ♕b1-b2+
     2 ♗d2-c3#

c) 1 ...   ♗c1-b2+
     2 c2-c3#

d) 1 ...   ♕b1xb3
     2 ♕a1xc1#

e) 1 ...   ♗c1xd2
     2 ♕a1xb1#

(9)

   1 ♕f6-b6

Threat 2 ♕b6-f2#. White allows Black to do his worst with the bishop and knight, but the checks may be met by discovered checks from the white rook.

a) 1 ...   ♔f1-e1
     2 ♕b6-b1#

b) 1 ...   ♘c3-e2+
     2 ♖g2-g7#

c) 1 ...   ♘c3-e4+
     2 ♖g2-b2#

d) 1 ...   h2-h1♘
     2 ♕b6-g1#

(10)

If you see the basic idea, then Speckmann's puzzle is easy, but if not then this innocent-looking position could prove troublesome.

    1   ♗f2-b6

Zugzwang.

a)   1   ...   ♔e2-d2
      2   ♕b7-f3   ♔d2-e1
      3   ♗b6-a5#

b)   1   ...   ♔e2-f1
      2   ♕b7-f3+ ♔f1-e1
      3   ♗b6-a5#

c)   1   ...   ♔e2-d1
      2   ♕b7-f3+ ♔d1-d2
      3   ♗b6-a5#

d)   1   ...   ♔e2-d3
      2   ♕b7-f3+ ♔d3-c4
      3   ♕f3-b3#

e)   1   ...   ♔e2-e1
      2   ♕b7-f3   ♔e1-d2
      3   ♗b6-a5#

If White had started with 1 ♗f2-a7, then lines a, b, c and e wouldn't have worked, while 1 ♗f2-c5 would have failed because line d wouldn't have worked.

(11)

    1   ♗h8-f6   ♔h5-g6
    2   h7-h8=♖ ♔g6xf6
    3   ♖h8-h6#

(12)

    1   ♕g7-f8

Zugzwang.

a)   1   ...   ♔f5-g5
      2   ♕f8-b4   ♔g5-f5

Or 2...♔g5-h5 3 ♕b4-h4#

      3   ♕b4-f4#

b)   1   ...   ♔f5xe5

      2   ♕f8-c5+ ♔e5-e4
      3   f2-f3#

c)   1   ...   ♔f5-e4
      2   ♔f7-e6   ♔e4-d4
      3   ♕f8-b4#

d)   1   ...   ♔f5-g4
      2   ♕f8-h6   ♔g4-f5
      3   ♕h6-f4#

(13)

White's queen needs to have access to a1, so the bishop has to hide itself away in the opposite corner to clear the way.

    1   ♗a1-h8   f5-f4

Or 1...♔f1-e1 2 ♕g5-c1#

    2   ♕g5-g7   ♔f1-e1
    3   ♕g7-a1#

(14)

    1   ♕g1-a7

Threat 2 ♕a7xc7#

    1   ...   ♖a6xa7

Or 1...♖a6xc6 2 ♕a7-a8#

    2   ♔g8-f7   ♔c8-d8
    3   ♖g7-g8#

(15)

    1   ♗c3-h8   ♘g8-f6

Or 1...♘g8-h6 2 ♕h7-g6#

    2   ♕h7-g6   ♔e6-e5

The point of White's first move is that Black is not stalemated here; indeed his king has to walk into a fatal pin.

    3   ♕g6-e4#

(16)

    1   ♗a2-g8   c3-c2
    2   ♖f2-f7   ♔a1-a2
    3   ♖f7-a7#

(17)

The trap is 1 e7-e8=♛, whereupon Black replies 1...d2-d1=♘+ and now White cannot mate in three more moves.

    1 e7-e8=♖   d2-d1♘+

Or 1...d2-d1♛ 2 ♖e8-h8+ ♛d1-h5 3 ♖h8xh5#

    2 ♔f2-g3   ♘d1-e3

Or 2...♘d1-c3 3 ♖e8-e1#

    3 ♖e8xe3   ♔h1-g1

The point of the rook promotion is that Black has this move; if White had a queen on e3, then Black would be stalemated.

    4 ♖e3-e1#

(18)

The idea is to force Black to promote both pawns to a knight. Then he can no longer promote to a queen, and White can switch plans.

    1 ♖a8-g8   f2-f1♘

Black is forced to promote to a knight because 1...e2-e1♛ is met by 2 ♖g8-g3+ ♛e1-c3 3 ♖g3xc3#

    2 ♖g8-d8   e2-e1♘

Or 2...e2-e1♛ 3 ♖d8-d3+ ♛e1-c3 4 ♖d3xc3#

    3 ♖d8-c8   ♘f1-e3
    4 ♖c8-c3#

(19)

White's first move is the key to the problem. After 1 ♗c6-a4? b7-b6 2 ♔c2-c1 b6-b5 3 ♔c1-c2 b5xa4 4 ♔c2-c1 a4-a3 5 ♔c1-c2 a3-a2, White's king is blocking c2. It follows that White must lose a tempo with his bishop and not with his king. However 1 ♗c6-e8? doesn't work, because after 1...b7-b5 the bishop cannot move to a4.

    1 ♗c6-b5   b7-b6
    2 ♗b5-a4   b6-b5
    3 ♔c2-c1   b5xa4
    4 ♔c1-c2   a4-a3
    5 ♔c2-c1   a3-a2
    6 ♘b4-c2#

(20)

    1 ♗c4-g8   a4-a3
    2 ♘h8-f7   ♔a1xa2
    3 ♘f7-e5+   ♔a2-a1
    4 ♗g8-a2   ♔a1xa2
    5 ♘e5-d3   ♔a2-a1
    6 ♘d3-c1   a3-a2
    7 ♘c1-b3#

8 Helpmates and Selfmates

'We'll get by with a little help from our friends.'
John Lennon and Paul McCartney

There have been some pretty bizarre positions in this book, but so far everything has conformed to the usual rules of chess. This is the point where we cross the frontier to fantasy chess.

Although there is a great variety of unorthodox chess problems, each with their own rules and stipulations, we will concentrate on the more well-known. This chapter is concerned with two of the most common types of unorthodox chess puzzles: the helpmate and the selfmate. Although they are related, they are best treated independently.

Helpmate

In orthodox puzzles, one side has a task (to win/to mate/to draw). It is always assumed that the other side (usually Black in compositions) will play the best moves to thwart these ambitions. In *Helpmates* the reverse is true.

As the name suggests, helpmates involve both sides helping to deliver checkmate. Normally Black moves first and in a specified number of moves White will deliver checkmate.

The concept is best illustrated by examples.

Norwood
1995

1	...	♝b8-h2
2	♘d1-f2#	

This is probably the simplest helpmate you will find. In normal chess there is no way that White could force checkmate with just a knight, but here Black is trying just as hard to ensure that he is mated!

The diagram overleaf is a helpmate in two. Black moves, White moves, Black moves again then White gives checkmate. The black king is vulnerable; the trick is to block the last flight square.

1	...	f2-f1=♝

A queen would have given check and destroyed the helpmate.

Norwood (corrected by **Burgess**)
1995

2   f7-f8=♘   ♗f1-h3
3   ♘f8-g6#

Checkmate.

Starting to get the idea? The trick with helpmates is to forget everything you have ever learned about chess (not permanently, hopefully) in the sense of you versus the opponent; you're both working together. One method is to try imagining possible mating positions, then see how you can arrange the pieces to reach them.

By their very nature, helpmates tend to involve the unexpected, so you shouldn't be looking at the most obvious moves. There is always a tendency to look for mating a king at the side of the board. Since helpmates value aesthetics highly you will find that the solutions are less mundane. Checkmating a king in the centre of the board is visually pleasing, and therefore more likely to be the solution.

An offshoot of the helpmate is the *Series Helpmate*. In a series helpmate,

Black has a series of moves (specified as series helpmate in n) at the end of which White delivers checkmate. This is the only move that White gets in the whole puzzle. Series helpmates can be very long, but the key is to pinpoint the overall idea, like the square on which the black king will be mated. In long series helpmates, remember there is the possibility of promoting (or underpromoting) pawns to assist in the mating net.

Selfmates et al.

This is a slightly different concept from helpmates. In a selfmate, the trick is to *force* Black to mate you. And one has to assume that Black will be doing everything possible to avoid giving mate. The selfstalemate takes the idea one stage further. In this White has to force Black to give stalemate.

1   **G. Paros**
             1956

Helpmate in three

2   **G. Paros**
           1958

3   **Loyd**
             1860

This is a helpmate in three.
There are three further parts to the
problem, all helpmate in three:
b) Move the white knight to d3;
c) Move the white knight to f3;
d) Move the white knight to h5;

This is a helpmate in three.
CLUE: As you might expect, you
have to finesse it in order to give
mate in the corner.

4   **Zilahi**
          1956

5   **Kardos**
          1956

This is a helpmate in two.
CLUE: The first move is totally
perverse, the move that you would
least expect given that Black is
supposed to be helping White.

This is a helpmate in seven; don't
despair, since with so few pieces
on the board it isn't impossible.
CLUE: Neither king moves in this
puzzle.

6   **Nunn**
1994

We end our helpmates with a truly impossible helpmate in four by Grandmaster Dr. John Nunn. Both myself and Murray Chandler were completely stumped by it. You'll get the solution in the next edition.

7   **Bartel & Kniest**
1965

This is a series-helpmate in four. Remember, Black has four moves, with White not moving at all. Then White gives checkmate in one.
CLUE: Only one of the pawns is promoted, and it becomes a rook.

8   **Levitt**
1994

Series-helpmate in 33. Yes, Black makes 33 consecutive moves, and White then mates in one.
CLUE: The first move is 1...♚b3-b2 and Black's king will visit every corner before it is mated.

9   **Dawson**
1927

This is a self-stalemate in four. White plays and forces Black to give stalemate after four moves.
CLUE: This composition is easily solved when you think about de-activating White's only piece.

10   **Popovski**
              1994

This is a selfmate in two. White moves, Black moves, White moves again, then Black is forced to give mate.

CLUE: Black is almost forced to give checkmate in two already, so don't upset the position too much.

Solutions

(1)

1	...	e5-e4
2	♕h7-a7	

This is the only waiting move White can play which doesn't disrupt the remainder of the solution – check it for yourself!

2	...	♔f4-e5
3	d3-d4+	♔e5-d5
4	♕a7-d7#	

(2)

1	...	h2-h1=♗

The theme of underpromotion continually recurs in helpmates.

2	♗f1-d3	♗h1-c6
3	♗d3-g6	♗c6-d7
4	♘b5-c7#	

The solutions to the other three parts involve Black promoting his h-pawn to the other three available pieces:

b)

1	...	h2-h1♕
2	♗f1-g2	♕h1-h5
3	♗g2-e4	♕h5-f7
4	♘d3-c5 mate	

c)

1	...	h2-h1♘
2	♗f1-b5	♘h1-g3
3	♗b5-c6	♘g3-f5
4	♘f3-g5 mate	

d)

1	...	h2-h1♖
2	♗f1-b5	♖h1-d1
3	♗b5-e8	♖d1-d5
4	♘h5-g7 mate	

(3)

1	...	♔f5-f6
2	♖g8-a8	♔f6-g7
3	♗f4-b8	

Note the way both the rook and bishop clear themselves away from the action, allowing the king to head into the corner. This is a recurring theme in helpmates.

3	...	♔g7-h8
4	♗b8-e5#	

(4)

1	...	♕b8xd6+
2	♔a6-b5	♔e4-d5
3	♘a2-c3#	

A very aesthetic finish.

(5)

1	...	f2-f1=♖
2	e2-e3	♖f1-f4
3	e3xf4	

Play is pretty much as expected for the next few moves.

3	...	e4-e3
4	f4-f5	e3-e2
5	f5-f6	

Now Black has to think about constructing a mating net. Note that the black king is not far from being in one already!

5	...	e2-e1=♖
6	f6-f7	♖e1-a1
7	f7-f8=♖	

Not a queen, since this would be check, thereby spoiling the solution.

| 7 | ... | ♖a1-a2 |
| 8 | ♖f8-f3# | |

The black pawn and rook simulate the effect of a back-rank mate.

(7)

| 1 | ... | h2-h1=♖ |

Now the king and the rook just have to change places: 2...♔g1-h2, 3...♖h1-g1, 4...♔h2-h1 and at this point White finally gets his big chance: ♖f4-h4#.

(8)

1...♔b3-b2 is the start of a massive 22-move king-trek: ...♔b2xa1-b2xc3xc4-b5-a6-b7xa8-b7-c7-d6-e5-f4-g3-h2xh1-g2-f3-e4xd5-e6.

Black has cleared a route for the pawn to come to the assistance of this glorious self-destruction. There follows 23...d7-d5 and then ...d5-d4-d3-d2-d1=♗. We still need to find a place for the king to be checkmated. Remember, it's a corner-to-corner, and there's still one corner we haven't visited yet. Black continues by playing 28...♗d1-c2, 29...♗c2xh7, 30...♔e6-f7, 31...♔f7-g8, 32...♔g8-h8 33...♗h7-g8. And after these 33

consecutive moves by Black, White can now play ♗a7-d4#.

(9)

1	♗e4-f5	♔e8-e7
2	♗f5xg4	♔e7-d8
3	♗g4-h5	

Black is powerless to prevent the entombment of the bishop.

| 3 | ... | ♔d8-e7 |
| 4 | g3-g4 | ♔e7-e6 |

Stalemate.

(10)

1   g3-g4

Whatever Black does, he cannot avoid a suicidal riposte by White.

| 1 | ... | ♕h4xh3 |

1...♕h4xg4 2 ♕e4-e6+ forces 2...♔g4xe6#, while 1...♕h4-g3 2 ♕e4-e5+ ♕g3xe5# also achieves White's self-destructive aim.

| 2 | ♕e4-f3+ | ♕h3xf3# |

9 Retro Puzzles

'I am too much of a sceptic to deny the possibility of anything.'
T.H. Huxley 1825-91

'You see but you do not observe.'
Arthur Conan-Doyle

When I was a young lad I bought myself a book entitled *The Chess Mysteries of Sherlock Holmes* by R. Smullyan. I liked chess, and I liked Sherlock Holmes, so I deduced that the combination must be good. Alas, I was in for a disappointment. The puzzles were like nothing I'd encountered before, involving 'retrograde' analysis – damned if I knew what that word meant.

Many years later I chanced on this book again. My unpleasant memories were quickly overcome and the puzzles suddenly became addictive. But time hadn't made them that much easier.

What are retrograde analysis problems in chess? You are given a diagram and basically you have to deduce what has happened, very much like the detective work of Conan-Doyle's character. Each individual puzzle may have its own stipulation; it might say simply, 'What was the last move played?' From a close examination of the pieces on the board you should be able to work this out. Or the puzzles may be like those we are used to: 'White to play and mate in one.' – but the solution will depend on your ability to work out what has happened.

Take this example, perhaps the simplest in Smullyan's collection (1957).

Black moved last; what was Black's last move, and White's move before that?

The first thing to notice is that there is a problem with Black's last move. We can say quite categorically that the black king could not have come from b7 or b8, since it would have been touching the king on c8. So it must have come from a7. But here we encounter another problem: would not the king be in check from the white bishop on g1? And the white bishop could not have moved to g1 since there is a pawn on h2. My own reaction was, 'Simple, the pawn has just under-promoted to a bishop!' Then I realised that White was of course going *up* the board.

Remember the words of that sagacious detective Sherlock; 'When one has eliminated the impossible, whatever remains, however improbable, must be the truth.' What tends to confuse the human eye is our obsession with looking only at the pieces on the board. Since we are concerned with what happened before, there could have been other pieces; i.e. a piece to block the check of the bishop perhaps.

So the starting position must have been (there could also be a black piece on a8):

White played 1 ♘b6-a8+ and Black replied 1...♚a7xa8.

Elementary, but only when you start to think about the possible rather than the probable.

Try this more sophisticated teaser by Smullyan.

1   **Smullyan**
1957

Your eyes do not deceive; the white king has fallen off the board and your task is to put it where it must have been (legally, there is only one square where it could have been).

CLUE: Tricky isn't it? Clearly the white king must have been obstructing the bishop's check to the black king. The only square it could have been on was b3, and it must have then moved. But how could it have been in double check? You should spot the solution *in passing*.

Now take a look at the diagram on the next page; despite being nearly a century old, this is a marvellous puzzle. White is to play and mate in two.

CLUE: If you have spent a long time scratching your head, then you are forgetting that this puzzle is in the retro-section; therefore, what the last move was must be relevant. As a further clue, it seems sensible to state what the accepted ruling is regarding *en passant*. Unlike castling, which is

2   **Amelung**
              1897

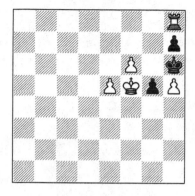

always assumed to be possible unless you are told or can prove otherwise, *en passant* is always assumed to be illegal unless you can prove otherwise.

3

This position has been reached after a mad time scramble and White has just smashed out his 40th move announcing checkmate. The chess press are crowding round to get the score of the game but the scoresheets of both players stop after White's

36th move. Neither player can remember what happened. Can you help?

CLUE: Take it step-by-step. The last move involved our old friend the *en passant*, but the white pawn came from c5 not a5; before that it had been on c4 where it moved to c5 with discovered check. But how could the king have been on b6 given that the queen is on b4? Think *en passant* again.

T. R. Dawson
1921

This retro has a deceptively simple condition: White to play and mate in two.

At first sight there are two solutions, 1 0-0-0+ and 1 ♔d2+. The real task is to work out why one of these 'solutions' is not valid. In this case, it is possible to prove the unlikely-looking fact that the rook on a1 is actually White's king's rook. There are six Black men missing; the tripled h-pawns must have taken five of these in order to reach their present positions, and the pawn on a5 must have made at least one capture. This accounts for all the missing Black men. Black's pawns must have made at least four captures to have reached their present positioons, and this exactly balances the four missing white men.

White's pawn captures occurred on e3, f4, g5, h6, a5 and either h3 or h4. As one of the missing Black men is his light-squared bishop, and all but one of the above squares are dark squares, we may deduce that the c8-bishop must have been captured on h3. At the moment when White played g2xh3, his bishop on f1 and rook on h1 must have been blocked in. But before White could play g2xh3, the c8-bishop must have been released by an earlier ...b7xc6. At this stage White's pawn must have already been on c7 (because there are no spare captures for it to play c5xb6xc7 later), and so Black must have already played ...c7xd6. Finally, note that once White has played c6-c7, Black's f8-bishop cannot escape from the squares f8 and e7. But in the diagram this bishop is on b6, so it must have escaped before c6-c7 and hence before ...b7xc6. Thus Black must have made three pawn captures (on c6, d6 and f6) before White played g2xh3, releasing the f1-bishop and h1-rook.

The only white pieces which were avilable to be captured at this stage were White's queen's rook, queen's bishop and queen, so these must have disappeared before g2xh3 was played. It follows that the queen's

rook has already been captured, and so the rook currently on a1 is the king's rook.

Thus White cannot castle and so the unique solution is 1 ♔e1-d2+ ♔h1-g2 (or 1...♗b6-g1 2 ♖a1xg1#) 2 ♘h3-f4#.

4   **C. Fox**
1931

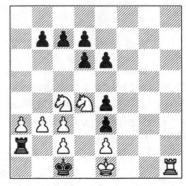

White to play and mate in two.

This problem is similar to the previous example. Finding the solution is not difficult, nor is the solution the real requisite of the problem. The real challenge with this one is to work out why White doesn't have a mate in one.

(Remember that castling is always legal unless you can *prove* otherwise.)

In the diagram overleaf, White is to play and mate in one. By now you should be able to 'deduce' the 'solution' to the likes of these with no trouble at all. But as usual with retros, the key is to prove why your solution is valid.

5   **T. R. Dawson**
1925

CLUE: In order to work backwards, one has to employ continually the theme of discovered check. White's last discovered check is not too hard to spot, but the one that preceded is the key.

6   **T. R. Dawson**
1914

White to play and mate in two. Dawson seemed to have a remarkable ability to hide an intricate retro behind a standard-looking problem.

CLUE: As usual, there is a problem with Black's last move. It cannot

have been a king move, so we have to focus on the pawns on d5 and f5. Neither could have come from the sixth rank where they would have been checking the king, so was the last move ...d7-d5 or ...f7-f5? Both allow an *en passant* with mate to follow, but only one move is legal. Remember, pawns do not lie.

7   **W. Keym**
1977

There are no hidden ideas behind this retro, you simply have to work out what the last move was.

CLUE: As to who played the last move, this should not be too testing: Black's only possible move was ...c7-c6 but this would make a nonsense of the position. White moved last and the obvious move is ♖a8-b8. Apart from its bluntness, there are other reasons why this could not be the solution. So the alternative is underpromotion to a rook, but was it on b8 or d8, and from a7 or c7?

The diagram overleaf is a more elementary one by Smullyan. It is

8   **Smullyan**
              1980

Black's turn to move; is 1...0-0 a legal move? Most of the white pieces have not even begun to participate, which leads one to expect a simple solution. But this factor led me astray and I spent a good deal of time barking up the wrong tree. As usual with retros, the key is discipline. Don't cut corners; work out, specifically, what has just happened.

CLUE: White's last move is easy enough to spot, but what about the penultimate? The configuration of black pawns tends to compromise certain knight manoeuvres.

Solutions

(1)

This is the only legal position since Black's b4-pawn is required to obstruct the check from the black rook. The black bishop has just given check on d5, White replies 1 c2-c4, and Black replies 1...b4xc3+ and 2 ♔b3xc3+. So the white king is on c3.

(2)

What was Black's last move? It could not have been with the king, which would have had to have come from g7, but then it would have been in check from the f6-pawn (which could not have come from f5, as the king is in the way). So it must have been the g-pawn moving to g5. But it could not have come from g6 since the king would be in check. Hence the move must have been ...g7-g5.

This allows an easy mate in two: 1 h5xg6 ♔h6-h5 2 ♖h8xh7#.

(3)

We can easily work back to this position in which the final moves were 38...♔b6-a6 (there might have been a white piece on a6) 39 c4-c5+ b7-b5 40 c5xb6#. Now the black king is in check, and for the same reason as before there must have been an *en passant*. So White's 39th move must have been 38 b5xc6+ in response to 37...c7-c5, forcing the black king to a6. But how could check from the bishop on g1 have arisen? Only by a further discovery from a piece which is no longer on the board, and must therefore move to a6, i.e. a knight.

It all goes back to the starting position:

From this point, the continuation was 36...♘b8-a6 37 ♘c5xa6+ c7-c5 38 b5xc6+ ♚b6xa6 39 c4-c5+ b7-b5 40 c5xb6#.

(4)

The move we all want to play is 1 0-0#. We have had the unusual castling theme several times in this book, so it has become almost a reflex reaction. But here it is simply not legal, since the white king must have moved. Why?

How could the king have got to c1? If it did not disturb the white king, then White must have played b2-b3, allowing the king to enter via b4, a3 and b2; later White played a2-a3 and d2xc3. However, in this case it is hard to see how Black's rook could have reached a2 without disturbing the white king, and one is tempted to say that it is impossible. But in this case what are all the Black pawns doing on the board? A composer never adds unnecessary material, so we must have overlooked a possibility...the possibility that the rook on a2 is a promoted pawn.

Black could have played his king to c1, and followed up by ...a3xb2 and b2-b1=♖. However, the black pawns already on the board must have made at least seven captures to have arrived at their present positions. Together with ...a3xb2, this makes eight captures, but there are only seven missing white men.

It follows that White's king must have moved, that he cannot castle, and that the solution is 1 ♔e1-f1.

(5)

The problem is Black's last move. It must have been with the d-pawn, since no other move could have been legal. The most subtle point is that the e-pawn has not just moved ...e7-e6. How do we know this? Well, I will try to explain.

If the e-pawn had been on e7, then the bishop on d2 must be a promoted piece (remember pawns do not lie; the bishop could not have left f8). If this is so then:

1) Black has lost a queen, two bishops, a knight, and three pawns (assuming there have been no other promotions);

2) The black bishop must have been captured on f8. This would leave six black pieces left to be captured.

The white pawns have made a total number of seven captures. This means that every black piece must have been used to enable them to cross so many files. So the black bishop could not have been captured on f8. Hence, the bishop on d2 is natural, and so the pawn cannot have just come from e7.

Note also that Black's last move could not have been ...♘e5-g4, because White's previous move must have been ♘g4-e3+, leaving the white king in an impossible check.

So it was the d-pawn that moved, but how do we know whether it came from d6 or d7?

White's last move must have been ♘d5-e3, giving discovered check, while simultaneously blocking the check from the black bishop. But this leads us into a problem with how the black bishop came to give check to the white king – it could not have just moved to d2, as there are no places to come from. So a black piece must have delivered a discovered check. There is no other culprit than the black knight which moved from e3-g4 with discovered check.

But this leaves us with another problem to resolve. With the white knight on d5 and the black one on e3, the black king is still in check from the white rook! And, as usual, the white rook can't have moved to h4. Bring on another discovered check!

The only piece left is the white bishop on b8. This could have been on f4, and then moved to b8 with discovered check. But, and here we come to the crunch, for the bishop to move to b8, it must have had a free path; i.e. no pawn on d6. So the pawn must have come from d7.

And if ...d7-d5 was Black's last move, we can cheerfully, and with a clear conscience, play 1 c5xd6#.

(6)

The striking feature is the disarray of the white pawns. Simple arithmetic shows that they have made a total of ten captures. This accounts for every captured black piece, including Black's light-squared bishop. So the bishop must have been released earlier to be taken by a white pawn. Thus the last move could not have been ...d7-d5.

This leaves us with ...f7-f5, allowing 2 g5xf6 and f6-f7#!

(7)

First, why was ♖a8-b8 not the last move? The same logic which proves that it could not have been Black to move in the diagram position applies; Black would not have had a legal move prior to this, except for ...c7-c6 which makes the position of the pieces on d8, e8 and f8 impossible. But this logic does not rule out a capture on b8; i.e. ♖a8xb8, since a black piece could have just moved to b8. We are left, therefore, with four possible candidate moves: ♖a8xb8, a7xb8=♖, c7xb8=♖ and c7xd8=♖. In each case there are four possible captured pieces, giving 16 possibilities in all.

A capture on d8 represents a problem. What black piece could have been captured by a pawn on c7? It cannot have been a bishop, rook or queen since they would not have had a square to move to d8 from. But if a knight had been on d8, what was Black's move prior to that? The only square for a knight to move to d8 from is e6, but this is taboo since the white king would have been in check. Hence, there could not have been a capture on d8.

We now know that the last move was a capture on b8: ♖a8xb8, a7xb8 or c7xb8. How to narrow it down further? As usual we have to consider the pawn captures made by White. We know, for instance, that both the rooks on d8 and e8 are promoted pawns, since the bishop on c8 hasn't moved. In order for the two pawns to promote to rooks, White must have made four captures (on c7 and d8, two times). This accounts for four black pieces. We also know that the bishop on f8 was captured on its own square, and that the h8-rook could not have been captured by a pawn (it could not have reached d8 to be taken by a white pawn as this would have involved leapfrogging the white king). This leaves only one black piece, i.e. the one that was captured on b8.

How to deduce what the piece captured on b8 was? Well there is only one piece that could not have been captured on c7 or d8: the queen's rook. So it must have been the rook that was captured last move on b8. This allows us to eliminate quickly another candidate move, ♖a8xb8, because the black rook must have just moved from a8 (the only square available). And then there were two.

The solution is found by returning to the question of pawn captures. If the last move was c7xb8=♖, then White would have needed an extra capture in order for the pawn to have got to c7. That would make six captures, but only five black pieces were available. Hence, we can finally conclude that the last move was a7x♖b8=♖.

(8)

White's last move was a2-a3; no question about that. So Black's move before that was a capture; i.e. the piece that moved before the white pawn. This piece must have been a knight since the white rooks never had any chance to enter the game. But which black piece captured the knight? The rook on a8 could not have captured the knight on a8, since all the entry squares are blocked. Was it captured on c8 by the bishop? No, since the knight would have come from d6, where it would have been checking the black king.

Clearly, none of the pawns are guilty, since they have not made any captures. This leaves us with either the king on e8 or the rook on h8. Whichever piece captured the knight, the conclusion is the same: Black cannot castle.

10 Sillies

'Mix a little foolishness with your prudence; it's good to be silly at the right moment.'
Horace

This is the chapter where anything goes, where we consider silly puzzles. Each puzzle will have its own stipulation, otherwise the normal rules of chess still apply. I cannot pretend that there is any real formula for solving these, but it helps to think laterally and have a vivid imagination.

One common type of silly puzzle is the retractor where you have to take back one or more moves, and play a different set of moves to achieve a given aim – usually mate. In attempting these it is important to bear in mind that a lot can happen in just one move for each side; a set of queens could have been captured for example. You must always be on the look-out for nuances. Could castling have been possible two moves ago? Was a pawn captured by *en passant*? Did a promotion occur?

These tricks tend to permeate most of these silly puzzles. Castling in an endgame would be highly unlikely, which is why our minds tend to miss this idea, which is why the composers put the concept into the position in the first place. Rather than rushing in to analyse variations, as you might in a real game, read the question carefully. Make sure that you understand what is being asked, then study the position to see how it relates to the question.

If, for example, the puzzle asks you to place one or more pieces on the board, consider how they might impact the position; the change will usually be subtle but decisive. Unless stated otherwise you must obey the laws of chess. Remember that moves are possible unless they are specifically illegal. This may sound like gibberish but it will become clearer as you get into the puzzles.

1 **Anon**

This is a take-back problem. White has just moved. You have to take back his last move and give checkmate instead.

CLUE: There is no law against castling in the endgame!

2 **S. Loyd**
1860

Here is another take-back (or retractor, as experts call it). White takes back a move and then gives checkmate.

CLUE: Think about the possibility of *en passant*.

3 **F. Vaird**
1910

This is more complex. Both White and Black take back their last move. Black then makes a different move, and White mates in one.

CLUE: Black's last move was to capture a queen on f5.

4 **E. Pogosiants**
1963

And now a very silly one. White to play and mate in a half-move!

CLUE: Do not take this too seriously.

5   **Fox & James**
1987

And even more silly. Deliver mate
in no moves!

6   **K. Fabel**
1946

Slightly more serious. Add a white
pawn to this position so that White
can then deliver mate in two.
CLUE: Note that if Black's g4-
pawn suddenly disappeared, 1
♗f7xg6 would be mate.

7   **W. Hartston**
1995

White to play and mate in one –
which of the pieces are black?

8   **K. Fabel**
1952

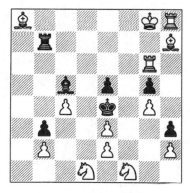

If, like me, you've missed some
pretty simple mates here is your
chance to shine. White is to play
and NOT checkmate in one. I had
no problems with this one.

9   **K. Fabel**
           1952

This a similar one by Fabel. Here White must find a series of moves to avoid winning! If only we had such problems in real chess.
CLUE: You should get this through a process of elimination.

10   **T. Dawson**
           1913

White is to play and deliver checkmate in 25 moves, moving only his knight!
CLUE: The plan is clear, but you have to lose a move first.

11   **S. Loyd**
           1858

This is a very well-known problem. The black king must be placed on a legal square so that White can then force mate in three.
CLUE: White's first move is 1 d2-d4.

12   **Anon**

Try this position in a bet and I guarantee you can win back the cost of this book. White to play and queen the pawn. Careful how you phrase it: bet that as White you can *queen the pawn*.

Solutions

(1)

Take back

1 &a7-a1

Instead of 1 &a1-a7, playing 1 0-0-0# would have been. These puzzles demand a fair amount of lateral thinking!

It should be noted that White could also take back &a7xpawn, knight or rook on a7. Skilful composers avoid such alternative possibilities.

(2)

This was the position before the previous Black and White moves.

1 ...   d7-d5

White could have played 2 ♕d2-c3#. Instead he captured the pawn *en passant*.

2 e5xd6

(3)

White takes back ♔g4x&f5 and Black then retracts &f1x♕f5.

Instead of 1...&f1xf5 2 ♔g4xf5 Black now plays the more helpful 1...&f1-h1, allowing 2 ♕f5-f2#.

(4)

White has just played h7-h8 (the half-move). The other half is =♕#.

(5)

Just turn the board around; the f4-pawn is giving mate to the king on e5.

(6)

Add a white pawn on h2. Then play 1 h2-h4 forcing 1...g4xh3 2 ♗f7xg6#.

(7)

It would be very easy to fall into the trap of thinking that the rook on a8 and the king on b8 are black pieces, with the remaining pieces white. This apparently allows White to play 1 ♘a7-c6#, but have another look at the position – Black has no previous move and so the position is illegal.

The solution is actually that the king on d8 is black and all the other pieces are white. White continues with 1 ♘a7-c6#, as before.

(8)

   1   ♖g6-c6+

The only move to avoid mate.

   1   ...   ♖b7xh7

(9)

1	c3-c4+	♖c2xc4
2	e3-e4+	♖c4xe4
3	♘g8-e7+	♖e4xe7
4	♘a8-c7+	♖e7xc7

The pleasing aspect to this solution is that although White tries very hard not to win, he doesn't lose either. It ends in stalemate.

(10)

1	♘f1-e3	♔a7-a8
2	♘e3-c2	♔a8-a7
3	♘c2-a1	♔a7-a8
4	♘a1-b3	♔a8-a7
5	♘b3-c5	♔a7-a8
6	♘c5-d7	♔a8-a7
7	♘d7xf8	♔a7-a8
8	♘f8-d7	♔a8-a7
9	♘d7-c5	♔a7-a8
10	♘c5-b3	♔a8-a7
11	♘b3-a1	♔a7-a8
12	♘a1-c2	♔a8-a7
13	♘c2-e3	♔a7-a8
14	♘e3-f1	♔a8-a7
15	♘f1-g3	♔a7-a8
16	♘g3xh5	♔a8-a7
17	♘h5xg7	♔a7-a8

Black could play ...h6-h5 from this point onwards, but White has the same mating line.

18	♘g7-h5	♔a8-a7
19	♘h5-g3	♔a7-a8
20	♘g3-f1	♔a8-a7
21	♘f1-e3	♔a7-a8
22	♘e3-d5	♔a8-a7
23	♘d5xe7	♔a7-a8
24	♘e7-d5	

Not stalemate!

24	...	h6-h5
25	♘d5-b6#	

(11)

The black king should be placed on h4.

   1   d2-d4   ♔h4-h5

Or 1...♔h4-g4 2 e2-e4+ ♔g4-h4 3 g2-g3#.

2	♕d1-d3	♔h5-g4
3	♕d3-h3#	

(12)

1	♗a3-d6	♔c8-b7
2	a5-a6+	♔b7-a8

Of course, the position is a theoretical draw, and your opponent will be getting impatient by now. But you should play until you reach the following position.

3	♗d6-c5	♔a8-b8
4	a6-a7+	♔b8-a8
5	♗c5-b6	♔a8-b7
6	a7-a8=♕+	

Now you claim your bet. You only bet that you would queen your pawn, you didn't say you would hold on to it!